Book

G

My Spelling Workbook

This book belongs to:

..........Ayaan....HBS....Patel..

Prim-Ed
Publishing
www.prim-ed.com

My Spelling Workbook *(Book G)*

Published by Prim-Ed Publishing 2011

2nd edition 2011

Reprinted 2012, 2015

Copyright© Prim-Ed Publishing 2011

ISBN 978-1-84654-786-7

PR–2286

Titles available in this series:
My Spelling Workbook *(Book A)*
My Spelling Workbook *(Book B)*
My Spelling Workbook *(Book C)*
My Spelling Workbook *(Book D)*
My Spelling Workbook *(Book E)*
My Spelling Workbook *(Book F)*
My Spelling Workbook *(Book G)*

Offices in:

UK and Republic of Ireland:
Marshmeadows
New Ross
County Wexford
www.prim-ed.com

Australia:
PO Box 332
Greenwood
Western Australia 6924
www.ricpublications.com.au

INTRODUCTION

Welcome to *My Spelling Workbook*.

This book and interactive download have lots of activities to help you learn to spell.

You should follow this method when you are learning to spell each word.

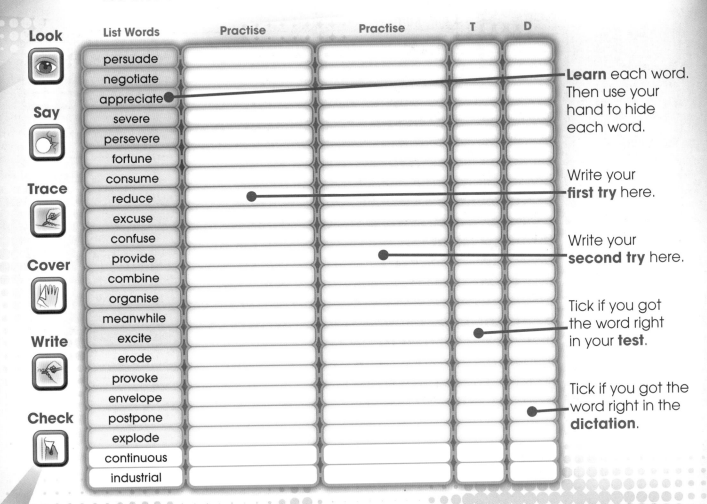

Look

Say

Trace

Cover

Write

Check

List Words	Practise	Practise	T	D
persuade				
negotiate				
appreciate				
severe				
persevere				
fortune				
consume				
reduce				
excuse				
confuse				
provide				
combine				
organise				
meanwhile				
excite				
erode				
provoke				
envelope				
postpone				
explode				
continuous				
industrial				

Learn each word. Then use your hand to hide each word.

Write your **first try** here.

Write your **second try** here.

Tick if you got the word right in your **test**.

Tick if you got the word right in the **dictation**.

Contents

unit 1

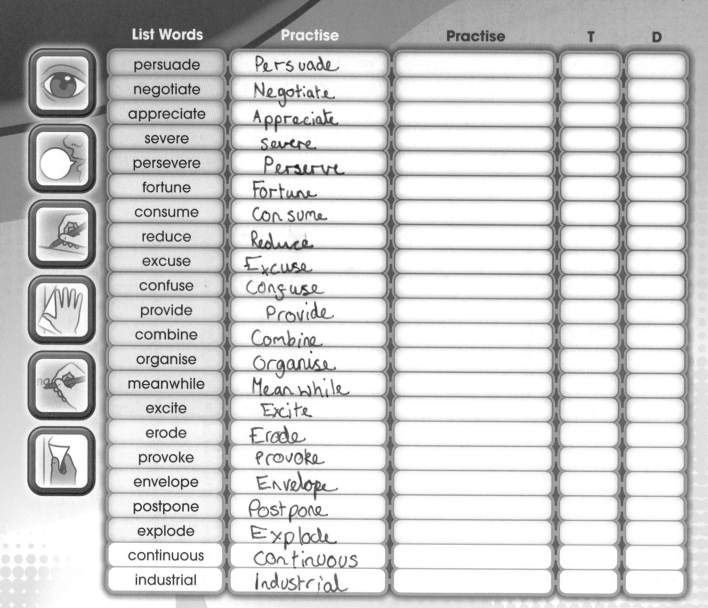

List Words	Practise	Practise	T	D
persuade	Persuade			
negotiate	Negotiate			
appreciate	Appreciate			
severe	Severe			
persevere	Perserve			
fortune	Fortune			
consume	Consume			
reduce	Reduce			
excuse	Excuse			
confuse	Confuse			
provide	Provide			
combine	Combine			
organise	Organise			
meanwhile	Meanwhile			
excite	Excite			
erode	Erode			
provoke	Provoke			
envelope	Envelope			
postpone	Postpone			
explode	Explode			
continuous	Continuous			
industrial	Industrial			

Verbs to Nouns

1. Change the verbs to nouns.
   Use a dictionary to help.

   (a) explode   Explosion
   (b) provide   Provider
   (c) appreciate   Appreciation
   (d) persuade   Persuader
   (e) organise   Orginisation
   (f) reduce   Reducer

Jumbled Words

2. Unjumble the list words.

   (a) uouoinntcs   Continuous
   (b) oeeenlpv   Envelope
   (c) eiaornsg   Orginise
   (d) rkeoopv   Provoke
   (e) eoopptns   Postpone
   (f) eeialwmnh   Meanwhile

crossword

3. Use list words to solve the crossword.

REDUCE
CONBINE
EXCUSE
CONSUME
PERSUADE
PROVOKE
ERODE
ORGANISE
ENVELOPE
MEANWHILE
APPRECIATE

Across

5. To stimulate favourably.
6. Eat or drink something.
8. Make something puzzling.
9. Convince somebody of something.
10. Wear away.
13. Put off.
17. At the same time.
18. Put in order.
20. Value somebody or something highly.
21. Harsh.

Down

1. Decrease.
2. Persist determinedly.
3. Join or mix together.
4. Forgive something.
7. Relating to industry.
9. Make somebody feel angry.
11. Supply.
12. Unchanged or uninterrupted.
14. Paper cover for a letter.
15. Discuss terms of agreement.
16. Great wealth or property.
19. Blow up or burst with force.

Vowel Sounds

4. Sort the list words according to the long vowel sounds.

Long '**o**'	Long '**i**'	Long '**u**'	Long '**a**'	Long '**e**'

List Words

- persuade
- negotiate
- appreciate
- severe
- persevere
- fortune
- consume
- reduce
- excuse
- confuse
- provide
- combine
- organise
- meanwhile
- excite
- erode
- provoke
- envelope
- postpone
- explode
- continuous
- industrial

Revision Words

- theatre
- popular
- fibre
- writer
- humour
- centre
- calculator
- particular
- diamond
- definitely

Missing Words

5. Complete the sentences using the list or revision words.

(a) That .... likes to use a lot of .... in his novels.

(b) The storm was so .... that they decided to .... the concert.

(c) We hope to .... shoppers to .... the number of plastic bags they use.

(d) If you .... in your training, you will .... be going to the Olympics.

(e) It will cost a .... to .... a trip to America!

Word Hunt

6. Which list or revision word(s) …

(a) have the prefix 'ex'? ....

(b) is a compound word? ....

(c) rhymes with 'tighter'? ....

(d) have five vowels? ....

Rule: When a word ends with 'e', the 'e' is usually dropped when a suffix beginning with a vowel is added.

Adding Endings

7. Complete the table.

	Verb	Add 's'	Add 'ing'	Add 'ed'
(a)	consume			
(b)	humour			
(c)	excite			
(d)	persevere			
(e)	consume			
(f)	persuade			

unit 1

Word Search

8. Find the list and revision words in the word search.

persuade	negotiate
appreciate	severe
persevere	fortune
consume	reduce
excuse	confuse
provide	combine
organise	meanwhile
excite	erode
provoke	envelope
postpone	explode
continuous	industrial
theatre	popular
fibre	writer
humour	centre
calculator	particular
diamond	definitely

The word search grid:

```
c o n f u s e r a l u c i t r a p
e l i h w n a e m e e k o v o r p
v d i a m o n d f x m m x e e c r
e r t a e h t u o c u v x x r a i
z t b n i s a c r i s p p m b l n
t e t e u u e e t t n l x x i c d
s p e g w o e g u e o y l e f u u
h o i o r u x r n d c z d p e l s
y l e t i n i f e d s o n r p a t
e e o i t i t a v v r w t o e t r
d v r a e t c d q e e n s p r o i
i n g t r n o l s x e s l o s r a
v e a e b o m e x c u s e p e s l
o q n j k c b h u m o u r u v s x
r e i e t a i c e r p p a l e e h
p o s t p o n e g p d m y a r l x
c n e s m s e v e d a u s r e p r
```

Homographs

The word 'excuse' is a homograph and can be pronounced in two ways to give two meanings.

9. Complete the following sentences.

(a) When it is pronounced 'excuse' to rhyme with 'choose', it is a verb and means ...

....

(b) When it is pronounced 'excuse' to rhyme with 'loose', it is a noun and means ...

....

Missing Vowels

10. Add the missing long vowel sounds.

(a) appreci....t.....   (b) f....br.....

(c) prov....k.....   (d) fort.....n.....

(e) negoti.....t.....   (f) sev.....r.....

(g) comb.....n.....   (h) organ.....s.....

(i) envel.....p.....   (j) the.....tr.....

(k) red.....c.....   (l) er.....d.....

aDDitional activities ✓

11. (a) Sort the list words according to the number of syllables they have.

(b) Write each of the list words in a question.

(c) Write the revision words in alphabetical order.

unit 2

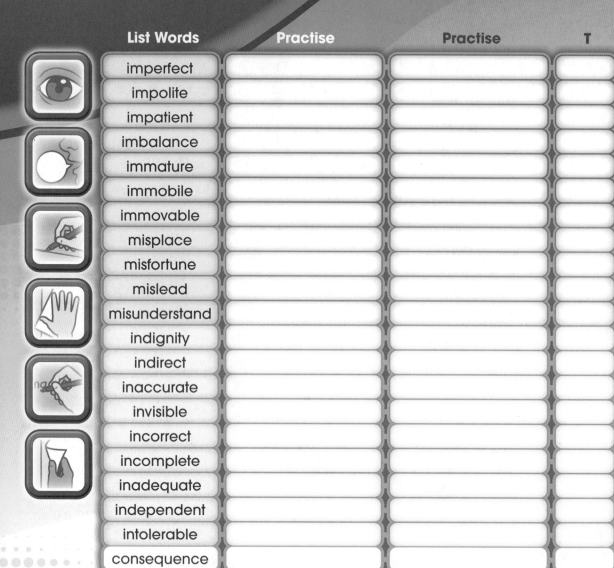

List Words	Practise	Practise	T	D
imperfect				
impolite				
impatient				
imbalance				
immature				
immobile				
immovable				
misplace				
misfortune				
mislead				
misunderstand				
indignity				
indirect				
inaccurate				
invisible				
incorrect				
incomplete				
inadequate				
independent				
intolerable				
consequence				
development				

prefixes

1. Use the correct prefix to complete the list words.

(a) ....balance

(b) ....place

(c) ....accurate

(d) ....understand

(e) ....dignity

(f) ....perfect

(g) ....tolerable

(h) ....lead

(i) ....visible

(j) ....movable

(k) ....direct

(l) ....mobile

(m) ....adequate

(n) ....complete

Suffixes

2. Add the suffix '**ly**' to these list words to turn them into adverbs. Use a dictionary to help you.

(a) impatient ....

(b) incorrect ....

(c) immature ....

(d) independent ....

(e) impolite ....

(f) incomplete ....

crossword

3. Use list words to solve the crossword.

Across

1. Motionless.
3. Not in a straight line.
6. Bad luck.
8. Not enough.
9. Opposite of find.
10. Cannot be seen.
13. Annoyed at waiting.
18. Inequality.
19. Deceive.
20. Growth.
21. Unbearable.
22. Flawed.

Down

2. Imprecise.
4. Wrong.
5. Not controlled by another.
7. Get the wrong idea.
11. Rude.
12. Result.
14. Unfinished.
15. Resolute.
16. Humiliation.
17. Childish.

prefixes

The prefixes 'in' and 'im' can both mean 'not' to make antonyms; 'im' is used before words beginning with 'b', 'm' and 'p'. Remember this rule and you will never use the wrong prefix again! Also remember that sometimes the prefix 'dis' is used to make antonyms of words beginning with 'p'; e.g. dispossess, disprove.

4. Write the correct prefix next to its meaning. Write two list words as examples of each prefix.

	Prefix	Meaning	Example
(a)		mistaken	
(b)		not	
(c)		not	

Unit 2

List Words

imperfect
impolite
impatient
imbalance
immature
immobile
immovable
misplace
misfortune
mislead
misunderstand
indignity
indirect
inaccurate
invisible
incorrect
incomplete
inadequate
independent
intolerable
consequence
development

Revision Words

antibiotic
autobiography
automatic
transplant
telescope
transfer
antiseptic
telepathy
fulfil
reference

Proofreading

5. Circle the list or revision words that have been incorrectly spelt. Rewrite the sentences correctly.

(a) If you use the teleskope, you can see that planet that is invisibel to the naked eye.

....

....

(b) It is incorect to believe that only one antibotic can cure all illnesses.

....

....

(c) The patient had to transpher to another hospital for his transplaunt operation.

....

....

Antonyms

6. Write a list or revision word with an opposite meaning.

(a) faultless .... (b) manual ....

(c) enough .... (d) well-mannered ....

(e) bearable .... (f) mobile ....

(g) good luck .... (h) helpless ....

(i) exact .... (j) tolerant ....

Secret Words

7. Find the secret words.

(a) Change 'tele' to 'horo' in 'telescope'. ....

(b) Change 'im' to 'auto' in 'immobile'. ....

(c) Change 'ence' to 'ee' in 'reference'. ....

(d) Change 'mis' to 'p' in 'mislead'. ....

(e) Change 'ity' to 'ation' in 'indignity.' ....

(f) Change 'auto' to 'pneu' in 'automatic'. ....

(g) Change 'mis' to 'common' in 'misplace'. ....

Jumbled Words

8. Unjumble the list and revision words.

(a) ncedirti .... (b) rfrneeeec ....

(c) ilsdaem .... (d) iseivibln ....

(e) tanerfrs .... (f) elhyatpet ....

Word search

9. Find the list and revision words in the word search.

imperfect
impatient
immature
immovable
misfortune
misunderstand
indirect
invisible
incomplete
independent
consequence
antibiotic
automatic
telescope
antiseptic
fulfil
impolite
imbalance
immobile
misplace
mislead

indignity
inaccurate
incorrect
inadequate

intolerable
development
autobiography
transplant

transfer
telepathy
reference

m	i	s	u	n	d	e	r	s	t	a	n	d	d	h	t	w	l	w
t	n	e	v	n	i	n	c	o	m	p	l	e	t	e	t	s	i	d
e	c	g	c	t	n	e	d	n	e	p	e	d	n	i	c	g	f	t
t	p	e	y	n	i	n	d	i	g	n	i	t	y	k	i	a	l	u
t	i	o	f	h	e	p	k	p	z	m	x	o	a	n	n	c	u	s
u	r	n	c	r	p	r	i	m	m	a	t	u	r	e	a	d	f	n
h	i	a	v	s	e	a	e	l	i	b	o	m	m	i	c	r	a	d
i	n	n	n	i	e	p	r	f	i	s	r	o	u	t	c	q	y	k
m	d	t	i	s	s	l	m	g	e	m	p	i	q	t	u	i	a	a
m	i	e	n	m	f	i	e	i	o	r	p	l	e	u	r	m	n	u
o	r	l	a	d	s	e	b	t	s	i	e	o	a	y	a	p	t	t
v	e	e	d	l	b	h	r	l	e	z	b	m	l	c	t	a	i	o
a	c	p	e	c	n	e	u	q	e	s	n	o	c	i	e	t	s	m
b	t	a	q	t	r	a	n	s	p	l	a	n	t	b	t	i	e	a
l	d	t	u	a	i	n	c	o	r	r	e	c	t	u	n	e	p	t
e	p	h	a	m	i	s	f	o	r	t	u	n	e	a	a	n	t	i
j	r	y	t	u	u	s	j	z	a	n	t	i	b	i	o	t	i	c
l	t	n	e	m	p	o	l	e	v	e	d	s	b	n	y	s	c	v
i	n	t	o	l	e	r	a	b	l	e	c	n	a	l	a	b	m	i

Small Words

10. Write list or revision words that contain these small words.

(a) me ....
(b) tie ....
(c) dent ....
(d) dig ....
(e) rap ....
(f) ace ....

additional activities

11. (a) Find more 'im' and 'in' words. Use a dictionary to help.

(b) Make five sentences using 'im' words and five using 'in' words.

(c) Sort the list words according to the number of syllables they have.

Suffixes: -ian, -ese, -ish, -er, -eer, -ist

List Words	Practise	Practise	T	D
Australian				
Italian				
Argentinian				
Iranian				
Vietnamese				
Portuguese				
Japanese				
Irish				
English				
Scottish				
jeweller				
builder				
photographer				
engineer				
auctioneer				
mountaineer				
scientist				
pianist				
dentist				
pharmacist				
material				
assessment				

Base Words

1. Write the list words that are based on these words.

(a) pharmacy ....

(b) science ....

(c) Italy ....

(d) Portugal ....

(e) mountain ....

(f) Ireland ....

(g) auction ....

(h) Scotland ....

(i) Australia ....

(j) assess ....

(k) Iran ....

(l) photograph ....

Missing Vowels

2. Fill in the missing vowels from the list words.

(a) m....t....r.........l

(b) p.........n....st

(c) j....w....ll....r

(d) d....nt....st

(e) J....p....n....s....

(f) ....ng....n.......r

(g) ....ngl....sh

(h) V.........tn....m....s....

(i) ....t....l........n

(j) b.........ld....r

(k) ....rg....nt....n.........n

crossword

3. Use list words to solve the crossword.

Across

1. Qualified person who treats teeth.
5. Rock climber.
6. A person who uses a camera.
8. Someone who conducts a bidding sale.
9. Somebody from Italy.
11. Relating to Ireland.
12. Someone who constructs something.
13. Someone who works with engines and machines.
17. Somebody who dispenses drugs.
18. Somebody who comes from Australia.
19. Marie Curie was a famous ......
20. Somebody who comes from Japan.
22. Evaluation.

Down

2. A person whose capital city is Edinburgh.
3. Fabric.
4. A person who makes ornaments for the body.
7. A person whose capital city is Lisbon.
10. A person whose capital city is Buenos Aires.
14. A person whose capital city is Tehran.
15. A person whose capital city is Hanoi.
16. British language.
17. Somebody who plays the piano.

General Knowledge

4. Match each clue to a list word.

(a) They live in Europe in a country famous for its pasta. ....

(b) This person fills your prescriptions. ....

(c) These people have the thistle as their national flower. ....

(d) Louis Pasteur was a famous … ....

(e) They live on an island continent. ....

(f) These people live in a South American country famous for football. ....

(g) Sir Edmund Hillary is a famous … ....

(h) You visit this person for a filling or extraction. ....

List Words

- Australian
- Italian
- Argentinian
- Iranian
- Vietnamese
- Portuguese
- Japanese
- Irish
- English
- Scottish
- jeweller
- builder
- photographer
- engineer
- auctioneer
- mountaineer
- scientist
- pianist
- dentist
- pharmacist
- material
- assessment

WORD HUNT

5. Which list or revision word(s) ...

(a) has only two letters from the name of the country? ....

(b) have six vowels? ....

....

(c) is an adverb? ....

(d) omits the letter 'l' from the name of the country? ....

(e) sounds as if it starts with 'f'? ....

(f) has four of the same letter? ....

Homonyms

Homonyms are words that are spelt the same and have the same sound, but different meanings.

6. Write sentences to show the two meanings of '**launch**'.

(a) launch (verb)

....

....

(b) launch (noun)

....

....

Revision Words

- caution
- authority
- exhaust
- applaud
- taught
- thought
- launch
- haunted
- preparation
- accidentally

Missing Words

7. Complete the sentences using list or revision words.

(a) The .... wanted to .... a rocket from the highest peak in the Alps.

(b) .... children are .... to eat sushi with chopsticks.

(c) With .... and armed only with a camera,

the .... slowly entered the supposedly

.... house.

8. Find the list and revision words in the word search.

Australian	Italian
Argentinian	Iranian
Vietnamese	Portuguese
Japanese	Irish
English	Scottish
jeweller	builder
photographer	engineer
auctioneer	mountaineer
scientist	pianist
dentist	pharmacist
material	assessment
caution	authority
exhaust	applaud
taught	thought
launch	haunted
preparation	accidentally

Word Worm Anagram

9. (a) Circle each list or revision word you can find in the word worm.

iengineeraltalianomaterialcpianisttuexhaustnbuilder

(b) Write the list or revision word you can make by unjumbling the remaining letters.

....

Shape Sorter

10. Write the list or revision word that fits in each shape.

(a)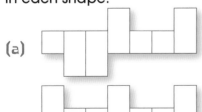

(b)

(c)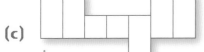

aDDitioNaL aCtiNities ✓

11. (a) Add to the list of nationalities and write them in alphabetical order.

(b) Add to the list of professions and write them in alphabetical order.

(c) Write five sentences, each using one word from the list of nationalities and one from the professions.

unit 4

ci, si, ssi, ss, ti

List Words	Practise	Practise	T	D
politician				
superficial				
physician				
electrician				
mansion				
expansion				
profession				
confession				
compassion				
session				
pressure				
fissure				
rotation				
revolution				
extinction				
conservation				
affection				
adaptation				
irrigation				
invention				
happened				
practise				

Missing Vowels

1. Fill in the missing vowels from these list words.

(a) .....nv.....nt.........n

(b) p.....l.....t.....c.........n

(c) .....rr.....g.....t.........n

(d) .....l.....ctr.....c.........n

(e) .....d.....pt.....t.........n

(f) s.....ss.........n

(g) s.....p.....rf.....c.........l

(h) pr.....f.....ss.........n

(i) .....xt.....nct.........n

(j) r.....v.....l.....t.........n

(k) pr.....ct.....s.....

(l) phys.....c.........n

Small Words

2. Write the list words that contain these small words.

(a) pen ....

(b) man ....

(c) act ....

(d) tin ....

(e) it ....

(f) pass ....

crossword

3. Use list words to solve the crossword.

Across

2. Process of enlargement.
5. Crevice.
6. Admission of wrongdoing.
8. Large house.
10. Line of work.
11. Occurred.
13. Shallow.
16. Supply of water to land or crops by means of channels.
18. Dying out.
19. Repeat in order to improve.
20. Government member.
21. Overthrow of government.

Down

1. Force.
3. A feeling of fondness.
4. A period devoted to a particular activity.
6. Protection of valued resources.
7. Created thing.
9. Sympathy.
12. A person who installs and maintains electrical equipment.
14. Adjustment.
15. A person qualified to practise medicine.
17. One complete revolution.

Suffixes

4. Sort the list words according to these endings.

ation	ssion	tion	sion

ution	cian	ssure	cial

List Words

- politician
- superficial
- physician
- electrician
- mansion
- expansion
- profession
- confession
- compassion
- session
- pressure
- fissure
- rotation
- revolution
- extinction
- conservation
- affection
- adaptation
- irrigation
- invention
- happened
- practise

Revision Words

- pyjamas
- binoculars
- athletics
- trousers
- species
- salmon
- moose
- tweezers
- carry
- surprised

Proofreading

5. Circle the list or revision words that have been incorrectly spelt. Rewrite the sentences correctly.

(a) It took the ilektrshian several days to rewire the manshon.

....

....

(b) Despite the work on conserfashon the samon in that river face extinshon.

....

....

(c) We put preshure on the politishin to change his views on our afletics club.

....

....

Sentences

6. Write each of these list or revision words in a sentence.

(a) binoculars ....

....

(b) rotation ....

....

(c) expansion ....

....

(d) superficial ....

....

Syl|la|bles

7. Colour all the parts of the six three-syllable list or revision words the same. Then write the words on the lines.

ex	ven	phy
sion	sion	pan
si	tinc	in
com	ex	cian
tion	le	pas
tics	ath	tion

....

....

....

....

....

....

Word search

8. Find the list and revision words in the word search.

politician
physician
mansion
profession
compassion
pressure
rotation
extinction
affection
irrigation
happened
pyjamas
athletics
species
moose
carry

superficial
electrician
expansion
confession
session
fissure
revolution
conservation
adaptation
invention
practise
binoculars
trousers
salmon
tweezers
surprised

```
d n b a s c n a f d o k s e c a r r y
e o i t d u o o t j n p v e s t g n z
n i n m w a p n i h z o y p s o v n i
e t o a b e p e s s l m i j b s o y d
p u c n i n e t r e n e a t a n i m x
p l u b o c k z a f r a t n a m b o v
a o l h c i i s e t i v p i s t a m n
h v a c o l t r u r i c a x c i o s a
t e r o m e n c t r s o i t e s o r i
p r s n p s f o n c p r n a i m g n c
e k t f a i x p i i e r u m l o v a i
r z r e s t v l h t t l i v f e n f t
u v o s s c d y n y a x e s n s k f i
s b u s i a g g s s s g e t e o i e l
s r s i o r q l a p g i i i h d s c o
e q e o n p n l k y c o c r s j y t p
r q r n t u m i h g n e l i r o p i k
p b s o q o z l m r p h c f a i j o v
e h k i n n o i s s e f o r p n d n g
```

Synonyms

9. Write a list or revision word with a similiar meaning.

(a) doctor ....

(b) sympathy ....

(c) creation ....

(d) astonished ....

(e) alteration ....

(f) occupation.........................

(g) admission ....

(h) growth ....

(i) house ....

(j) official ....

(k) transfer ....

(l) force ....

Base Words

10. Write the base words from which these words are made.

(a) conservation................ (b) politician ....

(c) irrigation .... (d) surprised ....

(e) rotation .... (f) electrician ....

(g) adaptation .... (h) expansion ....

(i) revolution .... (j) extinction ....

(k) confession .... (l) affection ....

additional activities

11. (a) Write the revision words in reverse alphabetical order.

(b) Sort the list words according to the number of vowels in each word.

(c) Write eight true or false statements using list or revision words.

List Words	Practise	Practise	T	D
bicycle				
biceps				
bikini				
bilingual				
triangle				
triplet				
trilingual				
quadrangle				
quadrilateral				
pentagon				
pentathlon				
hexapod				
heptathlon				
September				
octopus				
October				
octagon				
nonagon				
decade				
decagon				
questionnaire				
alcohol				

prefixes

1. Use the correct prefix to complete the list words.

(a) ....rangle

(b) ....ade

(c) ....pod

(d) ....plet

(e) ....rilateral

(f) ....cycle

(g) ....agon

(h) ....opus

(i) ....lingual

(j) ....kini

(k) ....thlon

(l) ....lingual

(m) ....angle

(n) ....ober

Matching

2. Match the prefixes and numbers.

(a) hexa •   • 5

(b) deca •   • 3

(c) bi •   • 4

(d) penta •   • 10

(e) oct •   • 7

(f) tri •   • 6

(g) quad •   • 8

(h) nona •   • 7

(i) sept •   • 2

(j) hepta •   • 9

crossword

3. Use list words to solve the crossword.

Across

4. Eight-sided shape.
5. US Defense Department.
7. Ten-sided geometrical shape.
8. Six-footed insects.
10. Large muscles in the upper arm.
11. The ninth month of the year.
12. One of three offspring born at one birth.
15. Nine-sided polygon.
16. Speaking two languages fluently.
18. Four-sided figure.
19. Speaking three languages fluently.
20. Athletic contest with seven events.

Down

1. A period of ten years.
2. Two-wheeled vehicle.
3. Three-sided figure.
4. Sea animal with eight legs.

6. The tenth month of the year.
9. A list of enquiries.
10. Woman's two-piece swimsuit.
13. Athletic contest with five events.
14. Four-sided courtyard.
17. Wine, beer, spirits.

Prefixes

4. Use a dictionary to help you complete the table below.

Prefix	Number	Greek or Latin	List Word Example	Meaning
(a) bi				Two-piece swimming costume
(b) tri	three			
(c) quadri			quadrilateral	
(d) penta		Greek		
(e) hexa				An insect; animal with six feet
(f) hepta				
(g) sept				
(h) oct				
(i) nona				
(j) deca		Latin		

List Words

bicycle
biceps
bikini
bilingual
triangle
triplet
trilingual
quadrangle
quadrilateral
pentagon
pentathlon
hexapod
heptathlon
September
octopus
October
octagon
nonagon
decade
decagon
questionnaire
alcohol

Incorrect Words

5. Write the list and revision words correctly.

(a) qestonaire ....

(b) pentafelon ....

(c) shedoule ....

(d) nunogone ....

(e) sirculat ....

(f) biseps ....

(g) seen ....

(h) Setember ....

(i) acurat ....

(j) hesistate ....

(k) oktopas ....

(l) trylingal ....

(m) kwadrlateral ....

(n) heptathilon ....

Letters into WORDs

6. Write four list or revision words using the letters on the octagon.

....

....

....

....

g a c
l h d
n f e o
t r u

Revision Words

accurate
hesitate
delete
scene
describe
refuge
schedule
umpire
scan
circulate

Word Meanings

7. Which list or revision word means ...

(a) able to speak three languages? ....

(b) a plan of work to be done? ....

(c) upper arm muscles with two attachment points? ....

(d) examine something with a beam of light? ....

(e) an athletic contest with seven events? ....

(f) an official enforcing sport's rules? ....

(g) ten years? ....

Word search

8. Find the list and revision words in the word search.

bicycle   biceps
bikini   bilingual
triangle   triplet
trilingual   quadrangle
quadrilateral   pentagon
pentathlon   hexapod
heptathlon   September
octopus   October
octagon   nonagon
decade   decagon
questionnaire   alcohol
accurate   hesitate
delete   scene
describe   refuge
schedule   umpire
scan   circulate

r	t	i	i	b	q	d	w	n	o	l	h	t	a	t	p	e	h	o
x	s	r	p	d	i	m	l	o	b	i	l	i	n	g	u	a	l	k
f	z	o	i	e	t	c	h	g	d	p	e	n	t	a	g	o	n	t
p	n	o	l	l	a	o	y	a	p	e	n	t	a	t	h	l	o	n
e	o	g	c	e	i	j	f	c	i	r	c	u	l	a	t	e	k	l
t	n	a	s	t	q	n	v	e	l	h	s	r	e	b	o	t	c	O
n	a	e	S	e	o	u	g	d	e	e	e	c	f	h	x	y	t	l
r	g	f	c	e	y	p	e	u	t	b	g	x	a	l	g	g	r	a
a	o	k	n	s	p	s	u	s	a	r	i	k	a	n	p	z	i	r
p	n	a	l	l	i	t	c	s	t	l	i	r	l	p	y	f	p	e
a	c	c	u	r	a	t	e	h	i	i	n	a	c	y	o	c	l	t
c	u	h	j	d	u	l	i	m	e	n	o	i	n	s	c	d	e	a
e	e	b	i	f	e	y	o	i	b	d	i	n	o	g	e	y	t	l
b	r	g	t	x	j	c	l	h	u	e	u	k	n	o	l	d	q	i
n	i	i	u	o	c	t	a	g	o	n	r	l	i	a	r	e	l	r
t	h	c	p	f	d	y	u	d	y	c	j	g	e	b	i	i	b	d
t	d	i	e	m	e	p	f	g	e	o	l	k	q	s	y	r	x	a
m	i	d	j	p	u	r	q	u	a	d	r	a	n	g	l	e	e	u
j	r	z	h	e	s	i	t	a	t	e	s	w	b	b	v	h	l	q

Missing Words

9. Complete the sentences using the list or revision words.

(a) The reporter had to .... the photos before he could ....
them via email.

(b) It had taken a .... for the tennis .... to learn three

languages and become ....

(c) The film director decided to .... the .... with the giant

.... sinking the ship.

Word Challenge

10. (a) Make at least ten words using the letters from the word below.

quadrilateral

(b) Circle the longest word you found.

additional activities

11. (a) Use a dictionary and add to the list of words with the prefixes, 'bi', 'tri' and 'quad'.

(b) Using one word with each prefix, write a sentence showing their meaning.

(c) Put the list and revision words into sets according to the number of syllables they have.

unit 6

-ence, -ance

List Words	Practise	Practise	T	D
difference				
silence				
commence				
absence				
independence				
patience				
conscience				
audience				
convenience				
experience				
chance				
balance				
distance				
appearance				
acceptance				
entrance				
substance				
instance				
assistance				
nuisance				
physical				
genius				

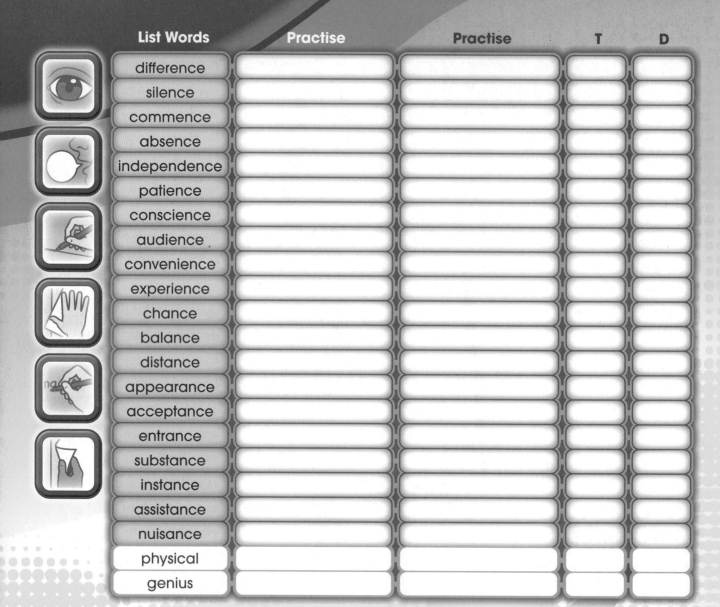

Suffixes

1. Fill in the missing suffixes '**-ence**' or '**-ance**'.

(a) consci..............

(b) nuis..............

(c) abs..............

(d) independ..............

(e) comm..............

(f) appear..............

(g) audi..............

(h) accept..............

(i) inst..............

(j) pati..............

(k) dist..............

(l) differ..............

(m) sil..............

(n) ch..............

(o) entr..............

(p) experi..............

Antonyms

2. Write a list word with an opposite meaning.

(a) exit ....

(b) noise ....

(c) similarity ....

(d) finish ....

(e) disappearance ....

(f) unsteadiness ....

(g) hindrance ....

(h) mental ....

crossword

3. Use list words to solve the crossword.

Across

1. Real and touchable.
7. The absence of sound.
8. The state of being away.
9. Somebody irritating.
12. A useful or helpful device or situation.
15. Knowledge or skill acquired.
19. Way in.
20. Matter or material.
21. Sense of right and wrong.
22. State of being unlike others.

Down

2. Freedom from control.
3. Way somebody looks.
4. Equilibrium.
5. Spectators.
6. Help.
10. The possibility of something happening.
11. Opposite of rejection.
13. Somebody with outstanding talent.
14. Capacity for waiting.
16. Example.
17. Begin.
18. Length between two things.

Adding Endings

4. (a) Write the list word made from each base word.

(b) Add the suffixes 's', 'ed', 'ing' or 'ly' to each base word to make new words.

	List Word	Base Word	New Words
(i)		silent	
(ii)		distant	
(iii)		appear	
(iv)		different	
(v)		convenient	
(vi)		patient	
(vii)		absent	

List Words

- difference
- silence
- commence
- absence
- independence
- patience
- conscience
- audience
- convenience
- experience
- chance
- balance
- distance
- appearance
- acceptance
- entrance
- substance
- instance
- assistance
- nuisance
- physical
- genius

Jumbled Words

5. Unjumble the pairs of the list or revision words.

(a) eeeeoooirxmpncnns .... + ...

(b) sssxbttncyuaei .... + ...

(c) eiauiablpclshtys .... + ...

(d) aieaeewlbdrnscrcvr .... + ...

(e) uiaeondnsncwt .... + ...

Sentences

6. Add the prefix 'in' to each of these words and write each new word in a sentence.

difference

experience

convenience

(a) ....

....

(b) ....

....

(c) ....

....

Revision Words

- monsoon
- tablespoon
- screwdriver
- wound
- youth
- coupon
- suitable
- pursuit
- sixty
- Africa

Word Hunt

7. Which list or revision word(s) ...

(a) is a continent? ....

(b) is a homonym? ....

(c) is a tool? ....

(d) are adjectives? ....

(e) have five vowels? ....

....

My Spelling Workbook G—Prim-Ed Publishing—www.prim-ed.com

Word Search

```
z d a e h i d w g d l w p a i t n u p
p i y c y n m i u i q h v i h i o n g
d s h n c d i f f e r e n c e u o s v
t t e e k e p a t i e n c e b s p w e
d a s s a p p e a r a n c e e r s c x
f n e b e e e t m n o p u o c u e u p
z c u a u n g c a o q h r a n p l c e
i e i o y d q e n n n j s g e b b o r
s y e t w e e u l e c s o b i w a n i
u b x c q n z c c b i e o s c l t v e
b i i m n c m n n s a d g o s a b e n
s u n s h e a e t a q t u z n c a n c
t g s q b s l a c i r a i a o i l i e
a e t t i j n i g n u t y u c s a e d
n n a u s c p b s v e o n e s y n n c
c i n o e q w k g u u m g e u h c c l
e u c A f r i c a t m r m z x p e e o
u s e o y t y c h a n c e o r r k i r
m k v c l r e v i r d w e r c s u u w
```

8. Find the list and revision words in the word search.

difference	silence
commence	absence
independence	patience
conscience	audience
convenience	experience
chance	balance
distance	appearance
acceptance	entrance
substance	instance
assistance	nuisance
physical	genius
monsoon	tablespoon
screwdriver	wound
youth	coupon
suitable	pursuit
sixty	Africa

Word Worm Anagram

9. (a) Circle each list or revision word you can find in the word worm.

(b) Write the list or revision word you can make by unjumbling the remaining letters.

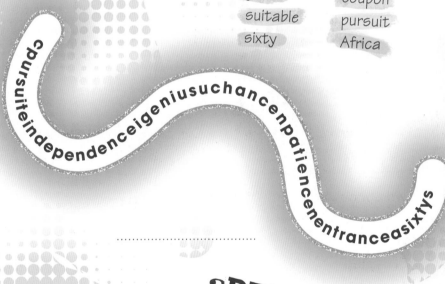

cpursuiteindependenceigeniusuchancenpatiencenentranceasixtys

....

Alphabetical Order

10. Write the revision words in alphabetical order.

(a) ....   (b) ....

(c) ....   (d) ....

(e) ....   (f) ....

(g) ....   (h) ....

(i) ....   (j) ....

aDDitioNaL aCtiNities ✔

11. (a) Write a meaningful sentence containing each list word.

(b) Write the list words in alphabetical order.

(c) Write a paragraph containing ten list or revision words.

List Words	Practise	Practise	T	D
Dancer				
Prancer				
anticipating				
exhausted				
poinsettia				
hibernate				
resolution				
sacred				
crackers				
myrrh				
frankincense				
potatoes				
elderberry				
roast				
commercial				
advertisements				
tradition				
decorations				
indulging				
programmes				
technology				
citizen				

Incorrect Words

1. Write the words correctly.

(a) mirh ....

(b) sitisen ....

(c) rowst ....

(d) ponseta ....

(e) pranser ....

(f) comershial ....

(g) tradishon ....

(h) resolushon ....

(i) crakers ....

(j) potaetos ....

(k) saykred ....

(l) exawsted ....

(m) dekorashons ....

(n) hibernaete ....

Small Words

2. Write the list words that contain these small words.

(a) pat ....

(b) acre ....

(c) no ....

(d) ram ....

(e) be ....

(f) set ....

crossword

3. Use list words to solve the crossword.

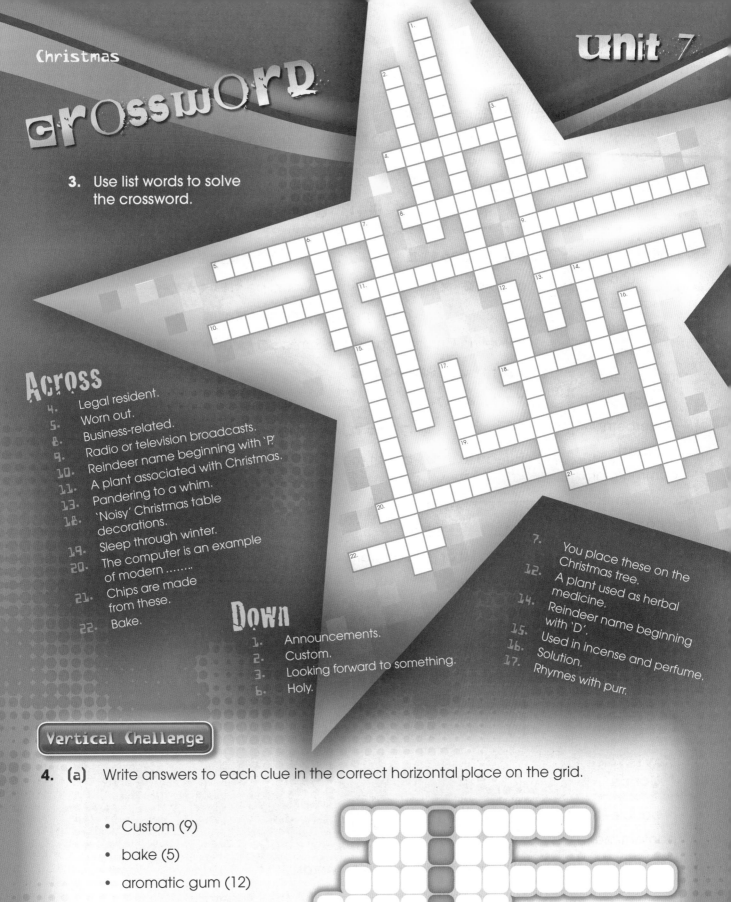

Across

4. Legal resident.
5. Worn out.
8. Business-related.
9. Radio or television broadcasts.
10. Reindeer name beginning with 'P'.
11. A plant associated with Christmas.
13. Pandering to a whim.
18. 'Noisy' Christmas table decorations.
19. Sleep through winter.
20. The computer is an example of modern ....
21. Chips are made from these.
22. Bake.

Down

1. Announcements.
2. Custom.
3. Looking forward to something.
6. Holy.
7. You place these on the Christmas tree.
12. A plant used as herbal medicine.
14. Reindeer name beginning with 'D'.
15. Used in incense and perfume.
16. Solution.
17. Rhymes with purr.

Vertical Challenge

4. (a) Write answers to each clue in the correct horizontal place on the grid.

- Custom (9)
- bake (5)
- aromatic gum (12)
- Santa's reindeer (7)
- purplish-black fruit (10)
- sleep through winter (9)

(b) Write the word in the highlighted vertical column. ....

(c) Write a clue for this word. ....

List Words

Dancer
Prancer
anticipating
exhausted
poinsettia
hibernate
resolution
sacred
crackers
myrrh
frankincense
potatoes
elderberry
roast
commercial
advertisements
tradition
decorations
indulging
programmes
technology
citizen

Secret Code

5. Use the secret code to find the list or revision words.

a	c	d	e	g	h	i	l	m	n	o	p	r	s	t	u	x
❋	✳	❄	❈	✲	✻	✷	●	○	■	▢	▱	▭	▲	▼	◆	❙

❄■▼✲✳✳▱▼✷❈❋ .... that ▱▢❋■✳✳▱ ....

and ✻❋■✳✳▱ .... would be ✳❙✳❋◆▲▼✳✳

.... after the yearly ▼▱❋✳✳▼✷▢■ .... of

delivering Christmas presents, Santa's ▱✷▲▢◆▼✷▢■ ....

was to avoid ✳■❄◆●✲✷■✳ .... in holiday television

▱▱✷❈▱❋○○✳▲ .... and food like ▱▱▢❋▲▼ ....

.... ▱▢▼❋▢▼❋✳▲ .... and turkey, and

instead to have a light meal and rest with all his reindeer.

Antonyms

6. Write a list or revision word with an opposite meaning.

(a) boring ....

(b) refreshed ....

(c) indecision ....

(d) charitable ....

(e) innovation ....

(f) dreading ....

Revision Words

bauble
pantomime
sledging
ceremony
shepherd
invitation
exciting
skiing
without
idea

Jumbled Words

7. Unjumble the list or revision words.

(a) prehedhs ....   **(b)** tinsietapo ....

(c) hitowut ....   **(d)** chtegnlooy ....

(e) biernathe ....   **(f)** viotaintin ....

(g) cedars ....   **(h)** krcercas ....

(i) ioeolutrns ....   **(j)** uggindlin ....

(k) ablebu ....   **(l)** aepostto ....

Word search

8. Find the list and revision words in the word search.

(word search grid)

Dancer
anticipating
poinsettia   exhausted
resolution   hibernate
crackers   sacred
frankincense   myrrh
elderberry   potatoes
commercial   roast
tradition   advertisements
indulging   decorations
technology   programmes
bauble   citizen
sledging   pantomime
shepherd   ceremony
exciting   invitation
without   skiing
Prancer   idea

Nouns and Verbs

9. Complete the table.

	Noun		Verb
(a)	skiing		
(b)			
(c)	decorations		
(d)	resolution		hibernate
(e)	invitation		
(f)	advertisements		

My Meanings

10. Write a definition for each of these words. Use a dictionary to help.

(a) commercial ....

....

(b) ceremony ....

....

(c) indulging ....

....

(d) sacred ....

....

additional activities

11. (a) Write the names of Santa's reindeers.

(b) Write these names in alphabetical order.

(c) Test your friends with the spelling of these names.

List Words	Practise	Practise	T	D
airbrush				
airstrip				
airlift				
airline				
airtight				
airborne				
airmail				
airspace				
aerial				
aerobatics				
aeroplane				
aerodrome				
aerobics				
aerosol				
supersede				
superficial				
superhuman				
superimpose				
superintendent				
superior				
prioritise				
potential				

Missing Vowels

1. Fill in the missing vowels from the list words.

(a) pr……r….t…s….

(b) ……r…s…l

(c) ……r…pl…n….

(d) s….p….rs…d….

(e) s….p….r………r

(f) ….irt….ght

(g) ………rb….rn….

(h) p….t….nt………l

(i) ………r….b….cs

(j) ………rsp….c….

(k) ………rl….n….

(l) s….p….r….mp….s….

(m) ………rstr….p

(n) s….p….r….nt….nd….nt

Alphabetical Order

2. Write the list words that end in 'e' in alphabetical order.

……………………………………………………………………………………………

……………………………………………………………………………………………

crossword

3. Use list words to solve the crossword.

Across

1. Paint spraying device.
3. Possible but as yet not actual.
6. Beyond human capability.
8. Metal rod for radio waves.
9. Without depth of character.
10. Spray can.
11. Stunt flying.
12. Landing field.
14. Lay something over something.
16. Transport of supplies by air.
17. Take over from.
18. Impermeable by air.
19. A runway.
20. Organisation providing a regular passenger air service.
21. Flying vehicle with wings.

Down

2. Manager.
4. Mail sent by air.
5. Space above territory.
7. Fitness exercises.
8. Carried by air.
13. Rank things according to importance.
15. Higher in quality.

Prefixes

The prefixes 'air', 'aer', and 'aero' all mean 'air'.
'Super' means placed above or over.
'Air' and 'super' are of Latin origin. 'Aer' and 'aero' originated in Greece.

4. Complete the table below. A dictionary may be useful.

	Prefix	List Word	Origin	Definition
(a)				transport by air
(b)		aerial		
(c)		aerodrome		
(d)		airline		
(e)				replace something less efficient
(f)		aerosol		
(g)		aerobics		
(h)				being near the surface

unit 8

List Words

airbrush
airstrip
airlift
airline
airtight
airborne
airmail
airspace
aerial
aerobatics
aeroplane
aerodrome
aerobics
aerosol
supersede
superficial
superhuman
superimpose
superintendent
superior
prioritise
potential

Secret Words

5. Find the secret words.

(a) Change 'ise' to 'y' in 'prioritise'. ....

(b) Change 'eye' to 'hind' in 'eyesight'. ....

(c) Change 'super' to 'in' in 'superhuman'. ....

(d) Change 'aero' to 'syn' in 'aerodrome'. ....

(e) Change 'while' to 'less' in 'worthwhile'. ....

(f) Change 'copy' to 'up' in 'copyright'. ....

(g) Change 'aer' to 'spec' to 'aerial'. ....

(h) Change 'pro' to 'ana' in 'program'. ....

Nouns and Adjectives

Remember: Nouns are naming words; e.g. the **airline**.
Adjectives describe nouns; e.g. **airline** food.

6. Underline the list or revision words in these sentences and classify them as nouns or adjectives.

(a) Airborne bacteria can cause contamination, so keep this product in an airtight container.

(b) It would be worthwhile obtaining the copyright for that book.

(c) It took a superhuman effort to organise the airlift and fly the children to safety from the war zone.

Nouns	Adjectives

Revision Words

toothache
eyesight
guidelines
whiteboard
copyright
worthwhile
spreadsheet
therefore
computer
program

Compound Words

7. Add a word to make these words into compound words from the list or revision words.

(a) ....ache

(b) ....space

(c) ....impose

(d) ....plane

(e) ....borne

(f) ....board

(g) ....lines

(h) ....strip

(i) ....human

(j) ....while

(k) ....fore

(l) ....tight

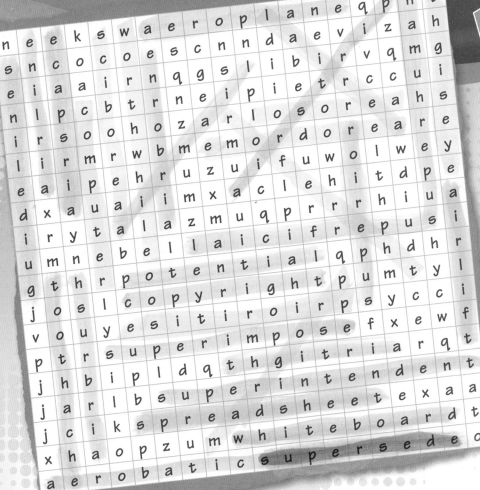

8. Find the list and revision words in the word search.

airbrush
airlift
airtight
airmail
aerial
aerodrome
aerosol
superficial
superimpose
superior
potential
eyesight
whiteboard
worthwhile
therefore
program

airstrip
airline
airborne
airspace
aeroplane
aerobatics
supersede
superhuman
superintendent
prioritise
toothache
guidelines
copyright
spreadsheet
computer
aerobics

Word Patch

9. (a) Write these 'air', 'aer', 'aero' and 'super' words in the correct place in the puzzle to find the hidden list or revision word.

airline   superhuman
superimpose   airstrip
airspace   superior
aerosol   aerial

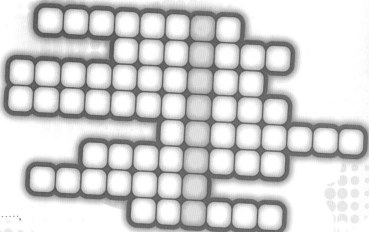

(b) The hidden word is ....

Small Words

10. Write list or revision words that contain these small words.

(a) rim ....
(b) man ....
(c) yes ....
(d) hit ....
(e) she ....
(f) ten ....
(g) rod ....
(h) her ....
(i) put ....
(j) too ....
(k) rip ....
(l) ace ....

additional activities ✔

11. (a) Add more 'aer' and 'super' words to the list words.

(b) Write six silly sentences using list or revision words.

(c) Write the list words, ordered according to the number of vowels in each.

List Words	Practise	Practise	T	D
azure				
seizure				
measure				
treasure				
pleasure				
leisure				
division				
decision				
erosion				
confusion				
conclusion				
transfusion				
explosion				
occasion				
abrasion				
euthanasia				
illusion				
seclusion				
collision				
exclusion				
nuclear				
immediately				

Missing Letters

1. Fill in the missing letters from the list words.

(a) divi.............n

(b) .....r.........sure

(c) n.....cl.........r

(d) transf.............on

(e) .....br.............on

(f) ....z...r....

(g) ....cc....s.........n

(h) s.............ure

(i) .....r....s.........n

(j) plea.............e

(k) ....m....ediat.............

(l) d....c....s.........n

(m) ....thana.............

(n) l.........s.............

Alphabetical Order

2. Write the list words that end with the letters '**sion**' in alphabetical order.

....

....

....

3. Use list words to solve the crossword.

Across

1. Wearing away.
2. Splitting into parts.
5. Using donated blood.
7. Particular time.
8. Act of determining size.
10. Deep blue.
13. Graze on the skin.
15. Enjoyment.
18. Final part of something.
19. Free time.
20. Crash.
21. False impression.

Down

1. Painless killing.
3. Convulsion.
4. Somebody has made a choice.
6. At once.
9. Blast.
11. Keeping out.
12. Jewels and precious objects.
14. Isolation.
16. Bewilderment.
17. Relating to the energy produced when atoms are split.

Adding Endings

4. **(a)** Write the list word made from each base word.

(b) Add the suffixes 'ed' and 'ing' to each base word, remembering the rules about adding suffixes to words ending with 'e'.

	List Word	Base Word	Add 'ed'	Add 'ing'
(i)		explode		
(ii)		divide		
(iii)		seize		
(iv)		seclude		
(v)		collide		
(vi)		exclude		
(vii)		confuse		
(viii)		conclude		

List Words

azure
seizure
measure
treasure
pleasure
leisure
division
decision
erosion
confusion
conclusion
transfusion
explosion
occasion
abrasion
euthanasia
illusion
seclusion
collision
exclusion
nuclear
immediately

Revision Words

quarantine
magazine
imagine
crevice
definite
advise
favourite
detective
monitor
parallel

Adverbs

An adverb is a word that adds information about a verb. Many adverbs end with the letters '-ly'.

5. Make these words adverbs. The spelling of these words may change. Use a dictionary to help.

(a) occasion .... (b) explosion ....

(c) confusion .... (d) definite ....

(e) exclusive .... (f) advise ....

(g) immediate .... (h) leisure ....

(i) conclusion .... (j) imagine ....

Antonyms

6. Write a list or revision word with an opposite meaning.

(a) dissatisfaction .... (b) vague ....

(c) reality .... (d) start ....

(e) understanding .... (f) inclusion ....

(g) least liked .... (h) divergent ....

(i) business .... (j) implosion ....

(k) union .... (l) later ....

Proofreading

7. Circle the list or revision words that have been incorrectly spelt. Rewrite the sentences correctly.

(a) There is definit evidence that the exploshin was caused by the colishon.

....

....

(b) Is it just an ilushon that models in a magazeen are so thin?

....

....

(c) A careful choice of lesher activities can bring you plesure and fitness.

....

....

Word search

8. Find the list and revision words in the word search.

azure
measure
pleasure
division
erosion
conclusion
explosion
abrasion
illusion
collision
nuclear
quarantine
imagine
definite
favourite
monitor

seizure
treasure
leisure
decision
confusion
transfusion
occasion
euthanasia
seclusion
exclusion
immediately
magazine
crevice
advise
detective
parallel

Nouns, Verbs and Adjectives

9. Sort these list and revision words under the following headings.

imagine   nuclear   detective
euthanasia   advise   definite
measure   illusion   azure

Nouns	Verbs	Adjectives

Word Challenge

10. Make as many words as you can from the letters in this word.

euthanasia

additional activities

11. (a) Make a list of jumbled words from the list and revision words. Give them to a friend to unjumble.

(b) Write down all the list or revision words with two syllables.

(c) Write definitions for six revision words.

List Words	Practise	Practise	T	D
dictionary				
primary				
ordinary				
secretary				
temporary				
boundary				
imaginary				
necessary				
military				
hereditary				
bakery				
cemetery				
surgery				
discovery				
archery				
mastery				
treachery				
slavery				
refinery				
battery				
government				
parliament				

Suffixes

1. Filling in the missing suffixes '**-ary**' or '**-ery**'.

(a) treach...............

(b) heredit...............

(c) necess...............   (i) slav...............

(d) arch...............   (j) milit...............

(e) refin...............   (k) batt...............

(f) ordin...............   (l) bound...............

(g) tempor...............   (m) discov...............

(h) prim...............   (n) surg...............

           (o) diction...............

           (p) mast...............

Alphabetical Order

2. Write the list words that would come between the words '**celebrate**' and '**number**' in the dictionary in alphabetical order.

celebrate

number

3. Use list words to solve the crossword.

Across

3. Border.
5. Branch of medicine.
6. Burial place.
9. Betrayal.
11. Armed services.
12. Power source.
17. Shop selling cakes and bread.
19. A sport using bows and arrows.
20. Fantasy.
21. Handed down through generations.
22. Condition of being owned by another.

Down

1. Expert skill.
2. A nation's legislative body.
4. Required.
7. Provisional.
8. Something learnt or found.
10. Book of word meanings.
13. Common.
14. Political authority.
15. Clerical worker.
16. Processing plant.
18. First in sequence.

Adding Endings

4. (a) Write the list word made from each base word.

   (b) Add the suffixes below to each base word to make new words.

List Word	Base Word	Add 's'	Add 'ing'	Add 'ed'
(i)	imagine			
(ii)	discover			
(iii)	refine			
(iv)	slave			
(v)	bake			
(vi)	master			

(c) Use the past tense of the words you created to complete these sentences.

(i) Mum .... for hours over the piles of ironing this weekend.

(ii) In the past, people commonly believed or .... the earth was flat.

(iii) In science we found out how oil was .... to turn it into useful products.

(iv) It was great when my brother .... tying his shoelaces.

Unit 10

List Words

- dictionary
- primary
- ordinary
- secretary
- temporary
- boundary
- imaginary
- necessary
- military
- hereditary
- bakery
- cemetery
- surgery
- discovery
- archery
- mastery
- treachery
- slavery
- refinery
- battery
- government
- parliament

Syllables

5. Colour all the parts of each of the seven list or revision words the same. Then write the words on the lines.

ty	ery	cue	dis
ti	ment	beau	due
sub	ful	ag	gov
ern	eigh	be	cov
bar	ary	in	im

....
....
....
....
....
....
....

Mixed-up Sentences

6. Unjumble the sentences.

(a) a is the of necessary check Using to spelling difficult words. dictionary

....
....

(b) secretary passes has members. the club to of issue The to new archery

....
....

(c) bakery queue at always break. There lunch is a that at

....
....

Revision Words

- barbecue
- analogue
- issue
- refuel
- skewer
- subdue
- beautiful
- queue
- body
- eighty

Plurals

7. Make the words plural.

(a) eighty ....
(b) surgery ....
(c) secretary ....
(d) primary ....
(e) body ....
(f) bakery ....
(g) battery ....
(h) discovery ....
(i) refinery ....
(j) dictionary ....
(k) boundary ....
(l) cemetery ....

Remember: Change the 'y' to 'i' and add 'es'.

40 My Spelling Workbook G—Prim-Ed Publishing—www.prim-ed.com

unit 10
word search

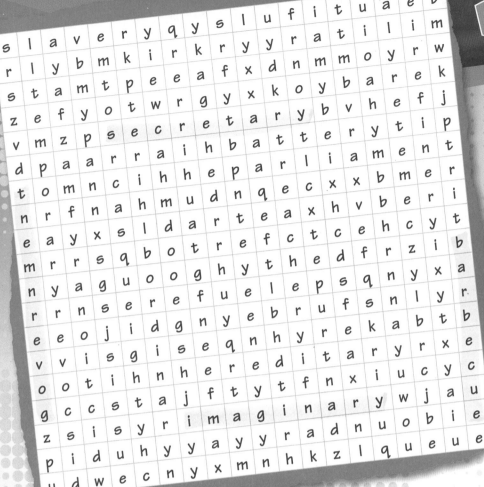

```
s l a v e r y q y s l u f i t u a e b
r l y b m k i r k r y y r a t i l i m
s t a m t p e e a f x d n m m o y r w
z e f y o t w r g y x k o y b a r e k
v m z p s e c r e t a r y b v h e f j
d p a a r r a i h b a t t e r y t i p
t o m n c i h h e p a r l i a m e n t
n r f n a h m u d n q e c x x b m e r
e a y x s l d a r t e a x h v b e r i
m r r s q b o t r e f c t c e h c y t
n y a g u o o g h y t h e d f r z i b
r r n s e r e f u e l e p s q n y x a
e e o j i d g n y e b r u f s n l y r
v v i s g i s e q n h y r e k a b t b
o o t i h n h e r e d i t a r y r x e
g c c s t a j f t y t f n x i u c y c
z s i s y r i m a g i n a r y w j a u
p i d u h y y a y y r a d n u o b i e
u d w e c n y x m n h k z l q u e u e
```

8. Find the list and revision words in the word search.

dictionary	primary
ordinary	secretary
temporary	boundary
imaginary	necessary
military	hereditary
bakery	cemetery
surgery	discovery
archery	mastery
treachery	slavery
refinery	battery
government	parliament
barbecue	analogue
issue	refuel
skewer	subdue
beautiful	queue
body	eighty

prefixes

9. Write the correct prefix for these list or revision words.

micro   re

anti   un

extra

(a) ....issue

(b) ....ordinary

(c) ....necessary

(d) ....discovery

(e) ....body

(f) ....surgery

Antonyms and Synonyms

10. Find the list or revision words with opposite meanings and then write a word with a similar meaning.

	Antonym	List/Revision Word	Synonym
(a)	optional	necessary	essential
(b)	permanent		
(c)	recall		
(d)	civilian		
(e)	ugly		
(f)	extraordinary		
(g)	real		
(h)	last		

additional activities

11. (a) Write five silly sentences using five list words within the sentences.

(b) Jumble eight revision words. Give to a friend to unjumble.

(c) Sort the list words according to the number of vowels in each.

unit 11

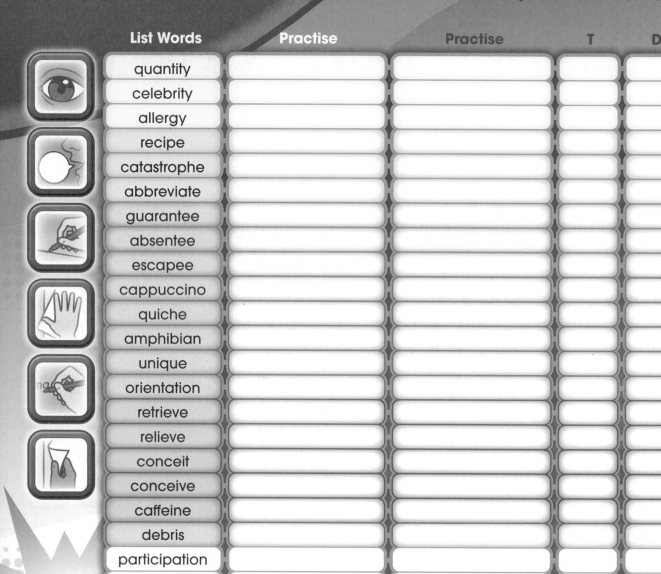

List Words	Practise	Practise	T	D
quantity				
celebrity				
allergy				
recipe				
catastrophe				
abbreviate				
guarantee				
absentee				
escapee				
cappuccino				
quiche				
amphibian				
unique				
orientation				
retrieve				
relieve				
conceit				
conceive				
caffeine				
debris				
participation				
outrageous				

Same Sound, Different Spelling

1. Add the correct letter(s).

(a) debr ....

(b) guarant..........

(c) conc..........ve

(d) q..........che

(e) amphib.....an

(f) cappucc.....no

(g) recip.....

(h) catastroph.....

(i) un.....que

(j) absent..........

(k) rel.........ve

(l) quantit.....

(m) abbr.....viate

(n) celebrit.....

(o) caff..........ne

(p) conc.........t

(q) retr.........ve

(r) escap..........

Jumbled Words

2. Unjumble the pairs of list words.

(a) trgsscpeoaaeueeou

.... + ...

(b) iaeieeeeabrvtvrlb

.... + ...

(c) ioiuiueiaartcptnnqp

.... + ...

(d) cmphbnrpeaiiaei

.... + ...

(e) uaieiqnydbrtst

.... + ...

y, e, ee, i, ie, ei, is

crossword

3. Use list words to solve the crossword.

Across

1. Fugitive.
5. Promise of quality.
7. Disaster.
9. Instructions for making food.
10. Famous person.
11. Shorten a word.
13. Positioning of something.
14. Only one (of a kind).
15. Land animal that breeds in water.
17. Wreckage.
18. Stimulant in coffee and tea.
19. Somebody not present.
20. Amount.
21. Think of or imagine something.

Down

2. Frothy milky coffee.
3. Excessive self-pride.
4. Get back.
6. Disgraceful.
8. Involvement.
12. Savoury tart.
15. Hypersensitivity to substance.
16. Alleviate.

Plurals

4. Follow this rule to make these words plural.

> When most words ending with 'y' are made plural, the 'y' is changed to 'i' and 'es' is added.

(a) quantity .... (b) allergy .... (c) celebrity ....

Proofreading

5. Find eleven mistakes and write them correctly on the lines below.

It's outraidjus that the escapea could have the conseat to be photographed on foreign shores happily eating quish and drinking capachino. He is now quite a sellebrity as he is in the unick position of having escaped successfully from our prison. Can you garantea the partisipashion of your government to help retreeve this absintea from there and into the hands of our police?

....

....

List Words

quantity
celebrity
allergy
recipe
catastrophe
abbreviate
guarantee
absentee
escapee
cappuccino
quiche
amphibian
unique
orientation
retrieve
relieve
conceit
conceive
caffeine
debris
participation
outrageous

WORD HUNT

6. Which list or revision word(s) ...

(a) has a silent 'w'? ....

(b) (i) have a soft 'c' sound?

....

....

(ii) Underline the letter that follows 'c' in each word.

(c) (i) follow the rule 'i' before 'e' except after 'c'?

....

....

(ii) does not follow this rule? ....

(iii) Circle the 'ie' or 'ei' in each word.

(d) has the most letters? ....

(e) has the fewest letters? ....

Suffixes

When adding a suffix beginning with a vowel to most words ending with 'e', the 'e' is dropped before adding the suffix.

7. Add one or more suffixes to the list and revision words below. Use a dictionary to help you.

-ism   -ion   -able   -ly   -ing   -ed

(a) conceive ....

(b) wrestle ....

(c) absentee ....

(d) answer ....

(e) retrieve ....

Revision Words

wrestle
answer
guide
plumber
tongue
column
debt
rhythm
emergency
accept

Synonyms

8. Write a list or revision word with a similiar meaning.

(a) shorten

....

(b) beat

....

(c) compass reading

....

(d) get back

....

(e) crisis

....

(f) truant

....

(g) ease

(h) struggle

(i) self-importance

....

(j) assurance

....

(k) language

....

(l) sole

....

y, e, ee, i, ie, ei, is

Word Search

9. Find the list and revision words in the word search.

quantity
allergy
catastrophe
guarantee
escapee
quiche
unique
retrieve
conceit
caffeine
participation
wrestle
guide
tongue
debt
emergency

celebrity
recipe
abbreviate
absentee
cappuccino
amphibian
orientation
relieve
conceive
debris
outrageous
answer
plumber
column
rhythm
accept

g	t	r	d	e	t	a	i	v	e	r	b	b	a	e	d	w	t	z
w	r	e	s	t	l	e	i	c	e	l	e	b	r	i	t	y	r	j
h	a	b	d	m	e	y	d	d	w	h	y	p	v	g	d	e	b	t
x	m	m	k	e	y	s	r	v	p	c	o	n	c	e	i	v	e	a
e	p	u	g	n	b	m	e	o	r	i	e	n	t	a	t	i	o	n
m	h	l	g	u	n	r	r	q	s	i	d	r	h	y	t	h	m	s
e	i	p	e	t	i	t	i	q	u	f	e	h	c	i	u	q	y	w
r	b	b	r	c	s	d	u	s	o	e	t	r	y	q	j	a	e	e
g	i	b	e	a	v	a	e	t	e	e	t	n	a	r	a	u	g	r
e	a	q	t	o	n	g	u	e	g	t	u	d	s	w	i	c	h	g
n	n	a	r	t	p	e	c	c	a	n	n	q	r	g	z	a	w	a
c	c	i	i	e	o	o	i	c	r	e	a	m	i	z	s	p	m	c
y	p	t	e	e	p	a	n	o	t	s	i	w	u	n	m	p	a	e
z	y	o	v	f	s	i	q	n	u	b	o	i	l	l	u	u	l	s
c	s	s	e	h	f	r	c	c	o	a	r	e	g	u	o	c	l	v
p	u	k	i	l	z	a	e	e	p	a	c	s	e	h	v	c	e	a
n	s	r	l	t	u	f	c	i	r	m	b	a	t	j	v	i	r	u
i	l	f	e	y	v	o	k	t	p	s	a	c	a	c	m	n	g	r
i	p	a	r	t	i	c	i	p	a	t	i	o	n	s	s	o	y	m

Origins

10. English is made up of words from scores of other languages. Can you find the country of origin of these words? Use a dictionary or the internet to help.

(a) debris ....

(b) allergy........................

(c) quiche........................

(d) recipe ....

(e) column ....

(f) catastrophe........................

Shape Sorter

11. Write the list or revision word that fits in each shape.

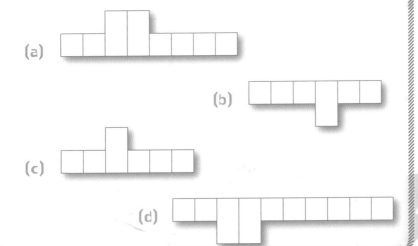

(a)

(b)

(c)

(d)

additional activities ✔

12. (a) Add suffixes to other list or revision words.

(b) Write five sentences using these new words.

(c) Write the list and revision words, showing the syllable breaks.

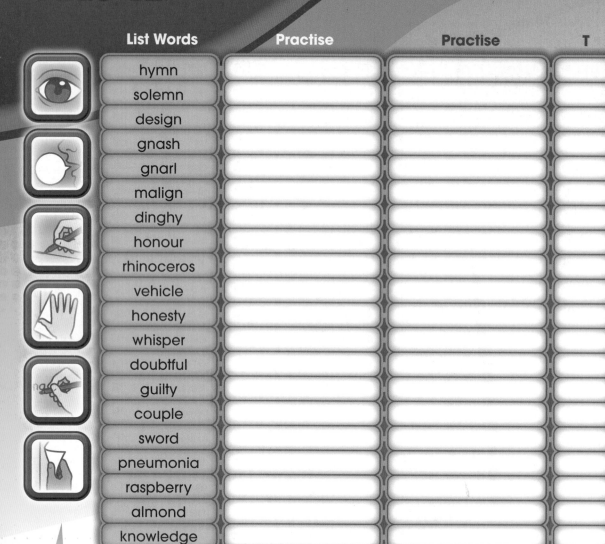

List Words	Practise	Practise	T	D
hymn				
solemn				
design				
gnash				
gnarl				
malign				
dinghy				
honour				
rhinoceros				
vehicle				
honesty				
whisper				
doubtful				
guilty				
couple				
sword				
pneumonia				
raspberry				
almond				
knowledge				
efficient				
sufficient				

Missing Silent Letters

1. Fill in the missing silent letters from the list words.

(a) .....neumonia

(b) w.....isper

(c) ras.....berry

(d) ve.....icle

(e) dou.....tful

(f) a.....mond

(g) .....narl

(h) hym.....

(i) s.....ord

(j) desi.....n

(k) .....onour

(l) r.....inoceros

(m) solem.....

(n) .....nowledge

(o) .....nash

(p) c.....uple

(q) g.....ilty

(r) ding.....y

Plurals

To make a word ending with 'y' plural, the 'y' is changed to 'i' and 'es' is added.

2. Make the list words plural.

(a) dinghy ....

(b) rhinoceros ....

(c) design ....

(d) raspberry ....

(e) hymn ....

(f) vehicle ....

(g) whisper ....

(h) almond ....

crossword

3. Use list words to solve the crossword.

Across

1. Speak softly.
5. Truthfulness.
7. Edible oval nut.
8. Small boat.
9. Means of transport.
12. Grave.
14. Two people sharing lives.
17. Plan and make something.
18. Long-bladed weapon.
20. Enough.
21. Criticise somebody spitefully.

Down

2. Religious song.
3. Massive horned mammal.
4. Information.
6. Respect.
8. Unlikely.
10. An edible red fruit.
11. Inflammation of lung.
13. Opposite of innocent.
15. Competent.
16. Grind your teeth.
19. Hard lump on a tree.

Silent Letters

4. For each silent letter, write a list word and another word(s) that have this silent letter.

Silent Letter	List Word	Another Word(s)
(a) k		
(b) p		
(c) u		
(d) b		
(e) w		
(f) o		
(g) h		
(h) g		
(i) n		

List Words

- hymn
- solemn
- design
- gnash
- gnarl
- malign
- dinghy
- honour
- rhinoceros
- vehicle
- honesty
- whisper
- doubtful
- guilty
- couple
- sword
- pneumonia
- raspberry
- almond
- knowledge
- efficient
- sufficient

Jumbled Words

5. Unjumble the list words.

(a) aeiounnmp ....

(b) cntiieffsu ....

(c) hrrnseocio ....

(d) wgedeknlo ....

(e) shwperi ....

(f) hlfuwtca ....

(g) cfenftiie ....

(h) snyhoet ....

(i) lbfuudto ....

(j) eenhtri ....

Antonyms

6. Write a list or revision word with an opposite meaning.

(a) innocent ....

(b) certain ....

(c) unpleasant ....

(d) deceitfulness ....

(e) inadequate ....

(f) inattentive ....

(g) praise ....

(h) cheerful ....

(i) incompetent ....

(j) shout ....

(k) separate ....

(l) ignorance ....

Revision Words

- already
- welfare
- until
- delightful
- awful
- skilful
- watchful
- wonderful
- either
- neither

Suffixes

7. Add the suffixes 'ing', 'ed', 'ly', 'ness' or 'able' to make new words.

List Words	New Words
(a) delightful	
(b) solemn	
(c) gnarl	
(d) skilful	
(e) honour	
(f) sufficient	
(g) malign	

unit 12

word search

```
l b e x y d i l a i n o m u e n p d y
y r t r g r n k u d o u b t f u l d k
t u a a a j r o n f x n d n y l a d n
l f u n y f n e m j l t w d l e r e o
i w v z g i l e b l x i z s r y h l w
u h x d e p n e i p a l k l w s i i l
g i l r e d h y w t s w a s c v n g e
j s a u v s r l c b h a o t o e o h d
k p f d f t i d w t e e r u u h c t g
w e a r d w n g n o l i r y p i e f e
d r o f h i a e n y y r t q l c r u w
u r n b r e i l i v n s l h e l o l o
n n o g y c f q p c e j o m e e s f n
a h o w i s q y q n i n l u a r s d d
g y y f s l h l o y o f u h d o n u e
n o f m n g a h p u l g f v l q y a r
a u c l n o m m r g x a u e n u v z f
s s d i w a t c h f u l m w r f m v u
h i d z f d m q e j d n j h k a r w l
```

8. Find the list and revision words in the word search.

hymn	solemn
design	gnash
gnarl	malign
dinghy	honour
rhinoceros	vehicle
honesty	whisper
doubtful	guilty
couple	sword
pneumonia	raspberry
almond	knowledge
efficient	sufficient
already	welfare
until	delightful
awful	skilful
watchful	wonderful
either	neither

Small Words

9. Write list or revision words that contain these small words.

(a) sign ....

(b) sole ....

(c) his ....

(d) now ....

(e) far ....

(f) nest ....

(g) at ....

(h) ash ....

(i) read ....

Word Hunt

10. Which list or revision word(s) …

(a) is a nut? ....

(b) have the suffix 'ful'? ....

(c) is a conjunction? ....

(d) has no vowels? ....

(e) is an object that floats? ....

(f) comes from Greek meaning 'of the nose'? ....

(g) comes from Latin meaning 'of air or wind'? ....

(h) is extremely sharp? ....

aDDitioNaL actiVities

11. (a) Write each of the revision words in a question.

(b) Sort the list words according to the number of syllables they have.

(c) Use a dictionary to write a definition for ten list words.

List Words	Practise	Practise	T	D
bouquet				
nursery				
ecology				
migrate				
crucifixion				
cultivate				
sacrifice				
environment				
resurrection				
horticulture				
propagate				
insect				
germinate				
fertilizer				
flourish				
foliage				
sunshine				
survival				
luxurious				
bountiful				
agriculture				
ecosystem				

Small Words

1. Write one list words that contain these small words.

(a) us ....

(b) if ....

(c) log ....

(d) our ....

(e) rat ....

(f) age ....

(g) fix ....

(h) germ ....

(i) ice ....

(j) shin ....

(k) stem ....

(l) cult ....

(m) vat ....

Verbs to Nouns

2. Complete the table.
Use a dictionary to help.

Verbs	Nouns
(a)	fertilizer
(b)	survival
(c) germinate	
(d) propagate	
(e)	crucifixion
(f) migrate	

CROSSWORD

3. Use list words to solve the crossword.

Across

1. Has three pairs of legs.
4. Light from the sun.
7. Giving up of something valued.
10. Cultivation of gardens.
12. Staying alive.
16. Surroundings.
20. Leaves.
21. Comfortable and expensive.
22. Move from place to place.

Down

2. Execution on a cross.
3. Grow well.
5. Garden centre.
6. Manure.
8. Organisms and their network.
9. Farming.
11. Prepare land for crops.
13. Rising from dead.
14. Abundant.
15. Start growing from seed.
17. Create new plants.
18. A collection of flowers.
19. Study of organisms and the environment.

Mixed-up Sentences

4. Unjumble the sentences.

(a) Christ. resurrection Easter celebrate the of At Jesus many

....

....

(b) set central I to the produce When rises. the heat, temperature heating in more the house

....

....

(c) cultivate have growing the to for soil in Farmers preparation season. new the

....

....

unit 13

List Words

- bouquet
- nursery
- ecology
- migrate
- crucifixion
- cultivate
- sacrifice
- environment
- resurrection
- horticulture
- propagate
- insect
- germinate
- fertilizer
- flourish
- foliage
- sunshine
- survival
- luxurious
- bountiful
- agriculture
- ecosystem

Revision Words

- colourful
- annual
- buffet
- variety
- temperature
- confectionery
- irresistible
- symbol
- lettuce
- onion

Secret Code

5. Use the secret code to find the list or revision words.

At the ✳■■◆✳● .... ✿▢▢▽✳✳◆●▽◆▢◆ .... show held in glorious ▲◆■▲✿✳■◆, ...

there was a ◆✳▢◆▽■ .... of stalls selling everything

from ✳▢■✳◆✳▽✳▢■◆▢■ .... to ✳◆▢▽✳●✳♥◆▢

.... On the ✳✳▢✳✳◆●▽◆▢◆ .... stall,

Mr Smith's enormous ▢■✳▢■ .... received a prize. His

wife won the top prize for her ✳▢●▢◆▢✳◆● ....

◎▢◆◎◆◆▽ .... of roses.

Rhyming Words

6. Write a list or revision word that rhymes with these words.

(a) thimble ....

(b) conviction ....

(c) psychology ....

(d) manual ....

(e) terminate ....

(f) nourish ....

Secret Words

7. Find the secret words.

(a) Change 'bou' to 'ban' in 'bouquet'. ....

(b) Change 'var' to 'anx' in 'variety'. ....

(c) Change 'fol' to 'marr' in 'foliage'. ....

(d) Change 'confec' to 'sta' in 'confectionery'. ....

(e) Change 'eco' to 'bio' in 'ecology'. ....

Sentences

8. Write each of these list or revision words in a sentence.

(a) environment ....

(b) buffet ....

(c) migrate ....

Unit 13

Word search

9. Find the list and revision words in the word search.

bouquet
ecology
crucifixion
sacrifice
agriculture
propagate

nursery
migrate
cultivate
environment
horticulture
insect
germinate
flourish
sunshine
luxurious
resurrection
colourful

buffet
temperature
irresistible
lettuce
fertilizer
foliage
survival
bountiful
ecosystem
annual
variety
confectionery
symbol
onion

```
        z e j m a e h n
            g f t s p o
            e a i m k i
            e r g r z q d n
      p y l t a u o v z u o
g u e
c t r     e n s k b i p o y t d o h g
r r n m   v c u c i l o l g e e r q o f
h e u e i v r u i n a   r t i r f o m u s h c c e
p o s c m n   t r f o t f w w r t i r f o m u s h c c e
b v r u i n a   i r e k f t s z p k l p w a f l l r e
o x v t r f o t f w w r t i r f o m u s h c c e
v i t i r i r e k f t s z p k l p w a f l l r e
l e n c e x i v a r i e t y o e r q o u e u w
n l o y u c i v a s s r r y c r n o l f c t x
  o x r l t o n b e m y y e a f l i r o l v
    x l e t i n e r o i r c t j e a u s u y
    t i v n u o j r c b d j u s q g o y c r
      i b e p b o r n i o i f y r b c e l s i k
      m f u q n u m e i e s e e l w e f t e o t r k
        w f o w l v q l n t a q p u j w a n s c e g l
        f f t m q g l o u a z c p j f q v i u p t m a
        a e c c j o a b b e o c r e h i i h o a a f v
        t e s e h u m   z t m b i s f t s i v r d i
        q d a s n y   w v k f b l n r w g t v
        i k e n s       h i u u u o i r r
        c c a i           c s x o m c u
        e j k               e e u r b d s
        f d             f u v h l y c w
```

Word Challenge

10. (a) Write words using the letters from the word below.

confectionery

(b) Circle the longest word you found.

Additional activities

11. (a) Write a list of items you might see at a horticulture show.

(b) Write a list of words with 'qu' in the middle.

(c) Write these 'qu' words in sentences.

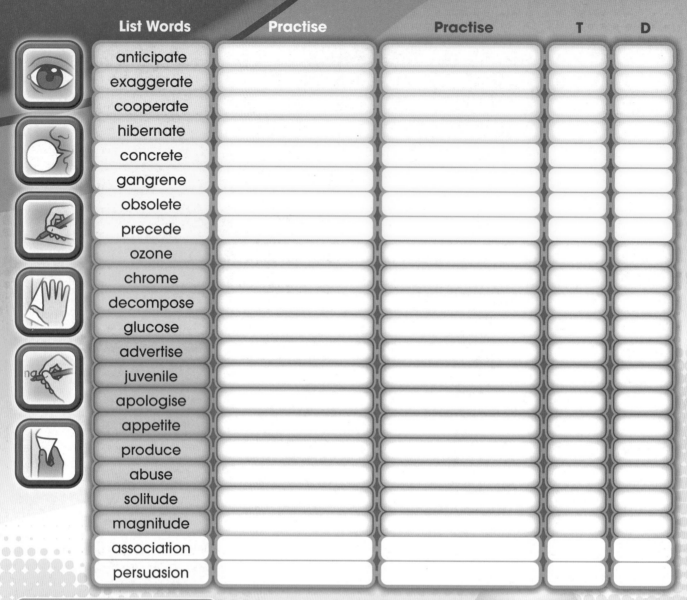

List Words	Practise	Practise	T	D
anticipate				
exaggerate				
cooperate				
hibernate				
concrete				
gangrene				
obsolete				
precede				
ozone				
chrome				
decompose				
glucose				
advertise				
juvenile				
apologise				
appetite				
produce				
abuse				
solitude				
magnitude				
association				
persuasion				

Missing Vowel Sounds

1. Add the missing vowel sounds from these list words.

(a) solit....d.....

(b) appet....t....

(c) chr....m....

(d) anticip....t....

(e) gluc....s....

(f) juven....l....

(g) concr....t....

(h) cooper....t....

(i) apolog....s.....

(j) oz....n.....

(k) gangr.....n.....

(l) magnit.....d.....

(m) hibern.....t.....

(n) juven....l....

(o) obsol....t....

(p) prec....d....

(q) prod.....c....

(r) decomp....s....

Word Hunt

2. Which list word(s) ... (a) have four syllables?...

(b) begin with a 'c' sound? ....

(c) have the letter 'c' making a soft sound? ....

(d) have double letters to keep the preceding vowel sounds short?

....

crossword

3. Use list words to solve the crossword.

Across

2. Rot.
5. Desire for food.
6. Say sorry.
8. Work together.
10. Manufacture something.
11. Sugar energy source.
13. Overstate something.
18. Chromium-plated metal.
19. Scale.
20. Isolation.

Down

1. Look forward to.
3. Form of oxygen.
4. Not used anymore.
5. Connection.
7. Come or go before something.
9. Harmful use of someone or thing.
12. Pass winter asleep.
14. Promote something.
15. Convincing somebody.
16. Death of tissue in body.
17. Youthful.
18. Hard construction material.

Homographs

4. The word 'abuse' is a homograph and can be pronounced in two ways to give two different meanings.

(a) When pronounced 'abuse' to rhyme with 'juice' it is a noun and means …

....

(b) When pronounced 'abuse' to rhyme with 'bruise' it is a verb and means …

....

Vowel Sounds

5. Sort the list words according to the long vowel sounds.

Long 'a'	Long 'e'	Long 'i'	Long 'o'	Long 'u'

List Words

anticipate
exaggerate
cooperate
hibernate
concrete
gangrene
obsolete
precede
ozone
chrome
decompose
glucose
advertise
juvenile
apologise
appetite
produce
abuse
solitude
magnitude
association
persuasion

Revision Words

population
vaccination
information
description
pension
official
concussion
social
country
trouble

Mixed-up Sentences

6. Unjumble the sentences.

(a) solitude. juvenile caused so was much The trouble, he delinquent into put

....

....

(b) doctors The that the could the could and flesh on gangrene his spread decompose. anticipate leg

....

....

....

(c) government the are going to The advertise vaccination the television. information about programme on

....

....

Small Words

7. Find small words hidden in these words.

(a) country ....

(b) apologise ....

(c) vaccination ....

(d) persuasion ....

(e) appetite ....

(f) abuse ....

(g) ozone ....

(h) pension ....

(i) gangrene ....

(j) chrome ....

(k) obsolete ....

(l) produce ....

Adding Endings

When a word ends with 'e', the 'e' is dropped when a suffix beginning with a vowel is added.

8. Complete the table below.

	List Word	Add 's'	Add 'ing'	Add 'ed'
(a)	precede			
(b)		troubles		
(c)				exaggerated
(d)			advertising	
(e)	decompose			
(f)		associates		

a-e, e-e, i-e, o-e, u-e

Word Search

9. Find the list and revision words in the word search.

anticipate
cooperate
concrete
obsolete
ozone
decompose
advertise
apologise
produce
solitude
association
population
information
pension
concussion
country

exaggerate
hibernate
gangrene
precede
chrome
glucose
juvenile
appetite
abuse
magnitude
persuasion
vaccination
description
official
social
trouble

```
x a e m o r h c i n f o r m a t i o n
e a w l m k o x l c o u n t r y a r v
l c o n c u s s i o n f t f q s d s a
i t r o u b l e s o p m o c e d v i c
n o i t a i c o s s a e a f t e e p c
e g l u c o s e g o p n p g a t r r i
v n o y r c z w t c o o p e r a t e n
u r f x s l n u g j p z e t e n i c a
j r f f a u o l a n u o t a g r s e t
o y i i x a i e n o l h i p g e e d i
j z c v h f t d g i a e t i a b g e o
s o i j e e p y r s t s e c x i p k n
s o a u r w i e e a i i e i e h r m i
p v l c f r r z n u o g x t b o o c e
e o n i q x c x e s n o o n a r d s g
r o n y t a s g q r i l a a s z u p o
c z a q w u e i o e w o t i o b c h x
w c g g q a t d l z p s p n w a g e p k
m g o b s o l e t e m a g n i t u d e
```

Nouns to Verbs

10. Complete the table below.

Noun	Verb
(a)	hibernate
(b) persuasion	
(c) information	
(d)	anticipate
(e)	exaggerate
(f)	cooperate
(g)	apologise
(h) vaccination	
(i)	advertise
(j) description	

Synonyms

11. Write a list or revision word with a similar meaning.

(a) communal ....

(b) superseded ....

(c) influence ....

(d) portrayal ....

(e) adolescent ....

(f) authorized ....

(g) overstate ....

(h) hunger ....

(i) importance ....

(j) seclusion ....

Additional Activities ✓

12. (a) Add to the list of long vowel sounds.

(b) Write a sentence for each long vowel sound.

(c) Test your friends with the spelling of the new words you have found.

List Words	Practise	Practise	T	D
dialogue				
rogue				
catalogue				
fatigue				
league				
intrigue				
plague				
colleague				
vague				
disguise				
guidance				
guardian				
guillotine				
guerilla				
guarantor				
guile				
ghoul				
ghetto				
gherkin				
ghastly				
feud				
amateur				

Missing Sounds

1. Fill in the missing sounds from the list words.

(a) ....ile

(b) ....astly

(c) collea.............

(d) dis.........ise

(e) ....oul

(f) catalo.............

(g) ....idance

(h) ro.............

(i) ....etto

(j) ....illotine

(k) intri.............

(l) ....arantor

(m) fati.............

(n) ....erkin

(o) lea.............

(p) ....erilla

(q) va.............

(r) ....ardian

Word Meanings

2. Write a list word to match each clue.

(a) Cleverness or cunning ....

(b) Layperson ....

(c) Soldier who carries out surprise attacks.............................

(d) It is edible ....

(e) A secret scheme or plot ....

(f) Not defined or definite ....

(g) A dispute ....

crossword

3. Use list words to solve the crossword.

Across

2. Legally responsible person.

3. Long violent dispute.

4. Area of city inhabited by minority.

8. Character's words.

12. Horrifying.

13. Somebody who assumes debts.

14. Machine for beheading people.

15. Somebody dishonest.

16. Fellow worker.

17. Epidemic.

Down

1. Unclear.

3. Mental or physical exhaustion.

4. Evil spirit.

5. Opposite of professional.

6. Group of sports clubs.

7. Leadership.

8. Something done to prevent recognition.

9. Small cucumber.

10. List of goods for sale.

11. Interest somebody.

13. Rebel.

14. Cunning and deceitfulness.

Alphabetical Order

4. Write the list words beginning with the letter '**g**' in alphabetical order.

Word Hunt

5. Which list words have …

(a) a long '**e**' sound?

Circle the long '**e**' sounds above.

(b) a long '**i**' sound?

Circle the long '**i**' sounds above.

Unit 15

List Words

- dialogue
- rogue
- catalogue
- fatigue
- league
- intrigue
- plague
- colleague
- vague
- disguise
- guidance
- guardian
- guillotine
- guerilla
- guarantor
- guile
- ghoul
- ghetto
- gherkin
- ghastly
- feud
- amateur

Proofreading

6. Circle the incorrect words and rewrite the sentence below correctly. Put in the missing punctuation.

(a) one of my coleeges bought a reversable jacket from my catalog

....

....

(b) you haven't fogotin how gastly the gerckin sandwiches were at the party

....

....

(c) do you think my gardiane will agree to be my garantor so I could buy a resonabel car

....

....

....

Secret Words

7. Find the secret words.

(a) Change the letters 'gu' in 'guile' to 'sm'. ....

(b) Change the letter 'g' in 'plague' to 'q'. ....

(c) Change the letters 'gue' in 'guerilla' to 'go'. ....

(d) Change the letters 'ver' in 'reversible' to 'spon'. ....

(e) Change the letters 'ble' in 'audible' to 'ence'. ....

(f) Change the letter 'e' in 'feud' to 'ra'. ....

Sentences

8. Write each of these list or revision words in a sentence.

(a) audible ....

....

(b) ghoul ....

....

(c) intrigue ....

....

(d) flammable ....

....

(e) separate ....

....

(f) amateur ....

....

Revision Words

- available
- comfortable
- reasonable
- flammable
- valuable
- audible
- legible
- reversible
- forgotten
- separate

60
My Spelling Workbook G—Prim-Ed Publishing—www.prim-ed.com

unit 15

word search

g	u	a	r	a	n	t	o	r	y	e	u	g	a	e	l	l	o	c
x	h	n	p	p	j	f	q	l	l	r	o	e	e	z	f	u	q	r
j	e	a	b	n	d	m	t	b	e	m	u	j	g	a	l	o	i	e
e	l	i	u	g	p	s	a	a	e	g	g	i	t	t	h	h	n	v
z	b	d	m	r	a	u	s	t	o	h	g	i	j	k	p	g	t	e
l	i	r	f	h	l	o	a	l	e	u	g	o	l	a	i	d	r	r
m	d	a	g	a	n	r	a	r	x	u	f	c	i	z	e	u	i	s
y	u	u	v	a	a	t	k	c	e	g	m	i	r	u	e	f	g	i
g	a	g	b	p	a	i	e	o	i	k	m	o	g	t	x	o	u	b
u	p	l	e	c	n	u	b	m	g	q	g	a	a	a	u	r	e	l
i	e	s	w	k	g	d	t	f	u	u	l	m	r	x	r	g	j	e
d	j	m	w	a	m	n	l	o	e	p	a	c	o	p	q	o	a	s
a	c	a	v	y	o	j	y	r	r	v	y	c	g	s	e	t	f	x
n	l	e	a	g	u	e	j	t	i	h	f	l	j	f	f	t	z	o
c	i	q	p	n	l	f	i	a	l	k	e	l	b	i	g	e	l	s
e	h	a	v	a	i	l	a	b	l	e	s	l	b	j	q	n	u	g
d	i	s	g	u	i	s	e	l	a	k	v	t	v	v	w	n	r	d
o	t	t	e	h	g	j	j	e	g	u	i	l	l	o	t	i	n	e
v	z	c	n	z	l	e	l	b	a	m	m	a	l	f	g	b	m	c

9. Find the list and revision words in the word search.

dialogue	rogue
catalogue	fatigue
league	intrigue
plague	colleague
vague	disguise
guidance	guardian
guillotine	guerilla
guarantor	guile
ghoul	ghetto
gherkin	ghastly
feud	amateur
available	comfortable
reasonable	flammable
valuable	audible
legible	reversible
forgotten	separate

Word Challenge

11. Make as many words as you can using the letters from the word below.

comfortable

Suffixes

10. Add the suffix 'ship', 'less', 'ly', 'ish' or 'ed' to these words.

(a) guardian ....

(b) vague ....

(c) legible ....

(d) audible ....

(e) catalogue ....

(f) ghoul ....

(g) guile ....

(h) comfortable ....

(i) plague ....

Remember: When adding a suffix beginning with a vowel to most words ending with 'e', the 'e' is dropped before adding the suffix.

additional activities ✓

12. (a) Write a paragraph using eight of the list words.

(b) Write the revision words in reverse alphabetical order.

(c) Sort the list words according to the number of syllables they have.

List Words	Practise	Practise	T	D
silent				
talent				
different				
evident				
intelligent				
president				
accident				
incident				
opponent				
confident				
distant				
vacant				
important				
instant				
migrant				
tolerant				
constant				
pleasant				
elegant				
arrogant				
soldier				
embarrass				

Missing Letters

1. Fill in the missing letters from the list words.

(a) toler...............

(b) intellig..............

(c) ....dier

(d) oppon...............

(e) evid..............

(f) tal..............

(g) embarr...............

(h) pleas..............

(i) arrog..............

(j) incid..............

(k) presid...............

(l) const..............

(m) accid..............

(n) migr...............

(o) eleg..............

(p) dist..............

(q) differ..............

(r) inst..............

Antonyms

2. Write a list word with an opposite meaning.

(a) humble ....

(b) unclear ....

(c) ally ....

(d) occupied ....

(e) irregular ....

(f) civillian ....

(g) near ....

(h) resident ....

(i) awkward ....

(j) trivial ....

3. Use list words to solve the crossword.

Across

3. Proudly contemptuous.
6. Make or become self-conscious.
9. Self-assured.
11. Obvious.
12. Mentally able.
13. Enjoyable.
16. Natural ability.
18. Steady.
19. Dissimilar.
20. Immediate.
21. Empty.

Down

1. Somebody moving from one place to another.
2. Head of state.
4. Adversary.
5. Event.
7. Somebody serving in an army.
8. Utterly quiet.
10. Broad-minded.
12. Significant.
14. Mishap.
15. Far away.
17. Stylish and graceful.

Nouns and Adjectives

The 'ant' and 'ent' endings can be used in adjectives;
e.g. an important man; and in nouns; e.g. the migrant arrived in 2001.

4. Complete the table below. If the list word is an adjective, write a phrase using the word. If it is a noun, write a definition.

List Word	Noun/Adjective	Phrase/Definition
(a) constant		
(b) talent		
(c) elegant		
(d) opponent		
(e) confident		
(f) migrant		
(g) soldier		
(h) arrogant		
(i) tolerant		

List Words

silent
talent
different
evident
intelligent
president
accident
incident
opponent
confident
distant
vacant
important
instant
migrant
tolerant
constant
pleasant
elegant
arrogant
soldier
embarrass

Revision Words

curious
ambitious
conscious
suspicious
delicious
jealous
marvellous
enormous
picture
occurred

Missing Words

5. Complete the sentences using the list or revision words.

(a) He is understanding and .... of people from .... backgrounds.

(b) His .... was........................... He would have to make up for his lack of height with skill in the boxing ring.

(c) It is .... that the .... is .... and rude, and will not be promoted to captain.

(d) The princess wore an .... gown when she met the French ....

(e) I am .... I can win the .... competition.

Small Words

6. Write list or revision words that contain these small words.

(a) red ....

(b) port ....

(c) bar ....

(d) tell ....

(e) side ....

(f) one ....

(g) leg ....

(h) old ....

(i) bit ....

(j) ale ....

(k) era ....

(l) can ....

Prefixes

7. (a) Write the correct prefix for these list or revision words.

 un

 in

(i) ....tolerant **(ii)** ....conscious **(iii)** ....elegant

(iv) ....pleasant **(v)** ....different **(vi)** ....suspicious

(b) Write sentences using an 'in' prefix word and an 'un' prefix word.

in ....

....

un ....

....

-ent, -ant

Word search

8. Find the list and revision words in the word search.

silent	talent
different	evident
intelligent	~~president~~
accident	incident
opponent	confident
distant	vacant
important	instant
migrant	tolerant
constant	pleasant
elegant	~~arrogant~~
soldier	embarrass
curious	ambitious
conscious	suspicious
delicious	jealous
marvellous	enormous
picture	occurred

q	e	s	s	t	i	s	i	n	t	e	l	l	i	g	e	n	t	z
p	q	r	s	u	j	s	u	d	t	n	e	d	i	f	n	o	c	d
t	i	e	u	o	s	p	s	o	e	z	e	v	y	a	l	t	w	n
g	n	m	t	t	v	p	f	a	i	r	e	l	i	b	r	k	j	n
i	t	a	p	n	c	m	i	s	r	c	r	l	i	d	h	y	d	a
t	n	j	t	o	e	i	a	c	u	r	i	u	e	s	e	t	d	r
n	e	g	o	s	r	d	p	r	i	o	a	l	c	g	x	n	s	o
e	l	i	l	q	n	t	i	t	v	o	i	b	e	c	a	e	t	g
r	a	s	e	v	p	i	a	c	n	e	u	t	m	d	o	n	v	a
e	t	u	r	v	k	t	z	n	n	a	l	s	i	e	d	v	t	n
f	s	o	a	a	n	v	r	p	t	i	t	l	t	b	z	j	s	t
f	j	i	n	a	a	m	f	h	l	l	h	s	o	e	m	e	u	o
i	h	c	t	c	a	c	c	i	d	e	n	t	n	u	n	a	o	p
d	s	s	a	r	e	i	d	l	o	s	a	h	s	o	s	l	i	p
e	i	n	p	r	e	s	i	d	e	n	t	s	r	c	c	o	r	o
d	t	o	r	i	p	l	z	h	d	f	i	m	a	p	v	u	u	n
p	h	c	z	t	e	t	c	e	d	k	o	q	b	n	b	s	c	e
t	o	j	f	n	f	l	c	x	w	u	i	t	j	v	t	h	z	n
c	d	r	j	p	x	y	d	b	s	c	l	m	i	g	r	a	n	t

Word Worm Anagram

9. (a) Circle each list or revision word you can find in the word worm.

(b) Write the list or revision word you can make by unjumbling the remaining letters.

marvellousvacantiinstantcsilentemigrantpleasanttcuriouspembbarrassr

....

Adding Endings

10. Complete the table.

List Word	Add 'ly'	Add 'ness'
(a) silent		
(b) conscious		
(c) jealous		
(d) vacant		
(e) pleasant		
(f) curious		
(g) ambitious		
(h) delicious		

additional activities ✓

11. (a) Use a dictionary to write a definition for ten list words.

(b) Jumble the syllables in the revision words and give to a friend to put back together.

(c) Write the list and revision words in alphabetical order.

List Words	Practise	Practise	T	D
sandwich				
valentine				
marmalade				
pavlova				
Morse code				
spoonerism				
arachnid				
pasteurise				
diesel				
hooligan				
cardigan				
volts				
biro				
teddy				
hygiene				
maverick				
leotard				
Braille				
Celsius				
python				
analysis				
permanent				

Extend Yourself

1. Unjumble each list word below. Then use a dictionary and other resources to complete a brief word history and definition for each eponym.

Jumbled Word	List Word	Word History
(a) vlaapvo	pavlova	Meringue dessert, filled with cream and topped with fruit, named after ballerina, Anna Pavlova.
(b) aeicmkvr		
(c) dedyt		
(d) goaolihn		
(e) aspturiees		
(f) daracing		
(g) ieseld		
(h) carniadh		
(i) soserniomp		

crossword

2. Use list words to solve the crossword.

Across

5. Large constricting snake.
6. Tight garment for gymnasts.
7. Writing system for visually impaired.
8. Long-sleeved knitted jacket.
10. Eight-legged organism.
13. Citrus fruit preserve.
15. Everlasting.
17. A scale of temperature.
18. A trademark for a pen.
19. A unit of electromotive force (plural).
20. Preservation of health.

Down

1. Unconventional person.
2. Accidental, amusing verbal error.
3. Violent youth.
4. Bread slices with filling in between.
9. Romantic greeting card.
11. Fuel for car engine.
12. Sterilize by heating.
13. System of signals using sound or light.
14. Study something closely.
15. A sweet cold dish.
16. A furry stuffed toy.

Alphabetical Order

3. Complete the table below by choosing fourteen list words and writing them in alphabetical order. Write a word or phrase associated with each; for example, biro – pen or write.

List Word	Associated Word

List Words

- sandwich
- valentine
- marmalade
- pavlova
- Morse code
- spoonerism
- arachnid
- pasteurise
- diesel
- hooligan
- cardigan
- volts
- biro
- teddy
- hygiene
- maverick
- leotard
- Braille
- Celsius
- python
- analysis
- permanent

Revision Words

- release
- purchase
- increase
- announce
- fierce
- potato
- echo
- patio
- multimedia
- email

Proofreading

4. Proofread this passage. There are eleven spelling errors and it is missing seven capital letters, four full stops, one question mark and two commas. Add the punctuation. Underline and rewrite the spelling errors correctly.

some of the list and revision words can be sorted into categories sanwiches paloves mamalade and potatos are foods araknids and feerse pihons are animals you can wear cardegans and leotardes under what category could you list braile and mors code

....

....

....

....

....

....

General Knowledge

5. Match each clue to a list or revision word.

(a) A lack of this can cause illness. ....

(b) A measure of temperature. ....

(c) A writing system invented by a man named Louis. ....

(d) A shortened form of 'electronic email'. ....

(e) A signal using sound or light. ....

(f) To go up in value or amount. ....

Small Words

6. Write list or revision words that contain these small words.

(a) time ....

(b) and ....

(c) arm ....

(d) one ....

(e) rail ....

(f) man ....

(g) tar ....

(h) die ....

(i) noun ....

(j) dig ....

(k) pot ....

(l) has ....

unit 17

Word Search

```
e q w o s e j e f w d t n r l y M o o
m s x h i m e n f g j w w i e d o x p
a v a c s a u i y y k n a g i d r a c
r d s e y i r t p d t w m v k e s s a
m x c s l l h n o r n a q c C t e a n
a u f a a e d e t a q d i d e m c n n
l z l n n r r l a z r r e u l m o d o
a r q t a a w a t r e d r b s k d w u
d o m t i x i v o v a i i h i x e i n
e a o m m m e p a k s c o e u s a c c
p e n l i l e m e e o o h v s y v h e
l u l u l a y d n r l i s n n e o e e
b c r i i d n k i i m t y g i c l s n
h s a c x o z l g a s a l q c d v a e
o r i b h i e a s t j p n j c s a e i
B g n t g a n y l d u l m e n u p r g
p e y t z l s o e c r e i f n n i c y
o p w h o i v e x c z h z t p t e n h
s p o o n e r i s m m l v b o w y i v
```

7. Find the list and revision words in the word search.

sandwich	valentine
marmalade	pavlova
Morse code	spoonerism
arachnid	pasteurise
diesel	hooligan
cardigan	volts
biro	teddy
hygiene	maverick
leotard	Braille
Celsius	python
analysis	permanent
release	purchase
increase	announce
fierce	potato
echo	patio
multimedia	email

Plurals

8. Make these list and revision words plural.

(a) sandwich ....

(b) potato ....

(c) echo ....

(d) teddy ....

(e) python ....

(f) patio ....

(g) biro ....

(h) spoonerism ....

Missing Letters

9. Fill in the missing letters from the list and revision words.

(a) h.........iene

(b) past.........rise

(c) incr.........se

(d) Cel...................

(e) anal.........is

(f) ann.........nce

(g) per...............ent

(h) mu...............media

(i) pav...............a

(j) rel.........se

(k) sa.........wich

(l) Bra...................e

(m) ara.........nid

(n) d.........sel

(o) l.........tard

(p) m...............alade

Additional activities

10. (a) Write a word history for all of the eponyms in the list words.

(b) Add to the list of eponyms.

(c) Test your friends with their meanings.

List Words	Practise	Practise	T	D
souvenir				
abseiling				
amusements				
catamaran				
helicopter				
tourism				
repellent				
navigation				
satellite				
security				
protection				
inoculation				
route				
intercontinental				
paragliding				
equator				
latitude				
longitude				
continent				
casualty				
technique				
strategy				

Incorrect Words

1. Write the list words correctly.

(a) cashalty ....

(b) satelight ....

(c) inoqulashon ....

(d) tecneek ....

(e) protekshon ....

(f) sueveneer ....

Nouns to Verbs

2. Change the nouns to verbs. Use a dictionary to help.

	Noun	Verb
(a)	amusements	
(b)	repellent	
(c)	security	
(d)	navigation	
(e)	protection	
(f)	inoculation	
(g)	paragliding	

CROSSWORD

Across

2. Course.
4. Plan.
6. Vaccination.
8. The distance north or south of the equator.
10. Disgusting.
11. Accident victim.
13. Preservation from injury.
15. A two-hulled boat.
17. Course plotting.
18. A flying machine that uses rotors.
20. Procedure.
21. Travel business.

Down

1. Memento.
3. Safety measures.
5. Between continents.
7. Recreational activities.
8. The distance east or west from Greenwich meridian.
9. Flying using a modified parachute.
12. An object placed in orbit.
14. Imaginary circle around Earth.
16. The art of descending by rope.
19. Land mass.

3. Use list words to solve the crossword.

Mixed-up Sentences

4. Unjumble the sentences. Add a capital letter and a full stop to each.

(a) swine inoculation good will flu us that protection against give

....

....

(b) rescue helicopter sent to a cliff abseiling casualty the who a was been from had

....

....

List Words

- souvenir
- abseiling
- amusements
- catamaran
- helicopter
- tourism
- repellent
- navigation
- satellite
- security
- protection
- inoculation
- route
- intercontinental
- paragliding
- equator
- latitude
- longitude
- continent
- casualty
- technique
- strategy

Revision Words

- cheque
- foreign
- tsunami
- humidity
- sweat
- mosquito
- carousel
- thermometer
- thousand
- double

Secret Code

5. Use the secret code to find the list or revision words.

a	c	d	e	f	g	i	l	m	n	o	p	q	r	s	t	u	v	w
❋	✳	❈	❋	❋	✳	✳	✳	●	○	■	◻	◱	◲	▲	▼	◆	❖	◗

The ▲●▼❋●●❋▼❋ .... ■❋❖❋❋●▼❋◻● ....

system had guided our ❋❋▼●○❋◻●■ .... across a

route that crossed the ❋◻◆❋▼◻◻ .... in the Atlantic

Ocean at zero degrees ●❋▼❋▼◆❋❋ .... and zero

degrees ●◻■❋❋▼◆❋❋ .... at the prime meridian.

By our hard ▲◗❋●▼ ...., we would soon reach the

❋◻◻❋❋❋■ .... African ❋◻■▼❋■❋■▼ ....

Secret Words

6. Find the secret words.

(a) Change 'tor' to 'lity' in 'equator'. ....

(b) Change 'tsun' to 'orig' in 'tsunami'. ....

(c) Change 'gliding' to 'chute' in 'paragliding'. ....

(d) Change 'maran' to 'logue' in 'catamaran'. ....

(e) Change 'che' to 'anti' in 'cheque'. ....

Word Meanings

7. (a) Match each word to its meaning.

(i) strategy •	• protection against disease
(ii) latitude •	• resistant to something
(iii) carousel •	• high moisture level
(iv) humidity •	• carefully devised plan of action
(v) repellent •	• room to manoeuvre
(vi) inoculation •	• circular conveyor belt

(b) Write a sentence containing two of these words.

....

Word search

8. Find the list and revision words in the word search.

abseiling
catamaran
tourism
navigation
security
inoculation
intercontinental
equator
longitude
casualty
strategy
foreign
humidity
mosquito

souvenir
amusements
helicopter

repellent
satellite
protection
route
paragliding
latitude

continent
technique
cheque
tsunami
sweat
carousel
thousand
thermometer
double

```
          s  b  m  v
          l  t  w  o
    n  i  p  a  r  t  s
    g  t  r  o  t  a  u  q  e
    s  a  t  e  l  l  i  t  e  u  r
          l  c  m  k  t  e  o  i  y        t  c  d
          h  u  z  u  g  u  t  o  c  h  a  s
          n  n  o  a  d  y  l  o  m  o  r  u        u  r
          a  i  o  j  e  a  q  r  u  o           w  e  g  q  x
          d  v  q  l  m  u  m  u  s  u           p  c  g  k  f  u  p
          p  d  i  u  y  s  g  z  a  s           e  q  n  l  m  u  v  l
          i  r  p  g  e  a  i  z  n  e  d  v  d     l  l  i  k  v  e     w  u
          u  x  o  t  a  c  e  r  d  l  f  b  t  w  l  i  l  s  r
          m  d  y  t  s  t  f  g  u  y  b  l  a  n  e  c  i  e  b  i  h
          l  a  t  n  e  n  i  t  n  o  c  r  e  t  n  i  e  c  z  k  g
          n  h  k  l  p  c  x  o  b  i  t  i  w  p  t  n  s  u  b
       z  h  u  m  i  d  i  t  y  n  i  a  v  s  j  z  e  b  r  r
       i  n  o  c  u  l  a  t  i  o  n  k  b  l  f  r  u  a  i
       l  o  n  g  i  t  u  d  e  o  w  x  q  q  e  t  q  n  t
       c  z  q  a  m  u  s  e  m  e  n  t  s  t  s  w  e  d  y
       t  h  e  r  m  o  m  e  t  e  r  p  u  r  v  h  f  i
       c  a  t  a  m  a  r  a  n  x  o  n  t  u  i  c  e
       t  n  e  n  i  t  n  o  c  a  p  o  k  e  z
       v  k  v  z  q  v  o  i  m  h  s  l  x  v  l
          p  a  r  a  g  l  i  d  i  n  g        x  j
          e  c  y  t  e  l  h                    j
             l     h  z  k  q                    f
                   v  i  x
                   b  q  x  q           e  x
                   n  g  i  e  r  o  f  t
                      d  o  u  b  l  e  u  s
                         d  g  b  o
                            l  r  w
```

Rhyming Words

9. Write a list or revision word that rhymes with these words.

(a) warren ....

(b) debt ....

(c) maturity ....

(d) stubble ....

(e) boutique ....

(f) fruit ....

Homophones

10. 'Check' and 'cheque' are homophones. Write a sentence for both words showing their meanings.

(a) check ....
....

(b) cheque ....
....

aDDitiONaL aCtiNities ✔

11. (a) Make a list of the seven continents.

(b) Make a list of some of the larger countries in these continents.

(c) Write these countries in alphabetical order.

Difficult words I Have FOUND

Word	Practise	Practise	Practise

My Spelling Workbook G—Prim-Ed Publishing—www.prim-ed.com

Difficult Words I Have FOUND

Word	Practise	Practise	Practise

Aa

Bb

Cc

Dd

Ee

Ff

Gg

Hh

Ii

Jj

Kk

Ll

Mm

Nn

Oo

Pp

Qq

Rr

Ss

Tt

Uu

Vv

Ww

Xx

Yy

Zz